Ronald C. Brosman
Oakville. Ontario

march 2, 1932.
#67

THE ART OF BIRD-WATCHING

A TREE-TOP OBSERVATION POST AT 120 FEET. OXFORD UNIVERSITY BRITISH GUIANA EXPEDITION. THE CHAIR IS HAULED UP BY THE THREE MEN SEEN BELOW.

Photographed by E. M. Nicholson.

(*Frontispiece*)

THE
ART OF BIRD-WATCHING
A PRACTICAL GUIDE TO FIELD OBSERVATION

By

E. M. NICHOLSON

Author of "Birds in England," "How Birds Live,"
"The Study of Birds"

ILLUSTRATED BY PHOTOGRAPHS
MAPS AND DIAGRAMS

The
Sports and Pastimes
Library

H. F. & G. WITHERBY
326 HIGH HOLBORN, LONDON, W.C.

First Published 1931

Printed for Messrs H. F. & G. Witherby
by J. & J. Gray, Edinburgh

PREFACE

BIRD-WATCHING is either the most scientific of sports or the most sporting of sciences. Which of these it becomes depends largely on the spirit in which it is pursued : both have had successful followers. Through this dual nature bird-watching forms an exception to every rule. As an outdoor recreation demanding knowledge, patience, and skill it comes nearest to shooting and fishing—the avenues by which many bird-watchers have in fact arrived. But it can be practised far more widely than either, and has the advantage, in convenience as well as in ethics, of leaving its quarry unharmed. Its inexpensiveness throws it open to all whose minds turn that way, for it has no bulky paraphernalia and bird-watching rights are not let for money. No occupation of such wide and tenacious appeal can be followed with such promise in so complete a variety of surroundings, from oceans and wild places to the hearts of great towns. As a science it is inseparable from ornithology, which depends increasingly on its success,

5

but its peculiarities are best shown by the fact that most of its outstanding figures have not been trained scientists. As a sport, on the other hand, it is distinguished by having an objective outside itself—to enlarge knowledge of birds—and by the fact that no one knows its rules. The purpose of this book is not plausibly to dispose of the mystery by inventing laws of no practical validity. It will all the same discuss how bird-watching is done, in the hope that from the discussion something constructive may emerge.

Having tried to set down on paper a coherent account of the subject the blemishes and inadequacies of this book are fresh in my mind. I have ruled out from the start any pretensions at encyclopædic treatment, and limited myself to describing the art of bird-watching as I conceived it. If these conceptions give rise to argument, and are shown to be mistaken or at least uncomprehensive, they will still have served their function. Before we can lay down the law we have still to understand that there is a definite art of bird-watching, towards which we are still groping : the more we discuss it the sooner it will be grasped.

I have obligations to many older bird-watchers, from Gilbert White to Eliot Howard and Julian

Huxley, for the fundamentals on which this book
is based. More immediately, I have to thank the
Editor of *Discovery* for the use of Figure 7 and
Mr. V. C. Wynne-Edwards for permission to include
Figures 7 and 13 ; Professor A. G. Tansley for permission to use Figure 8 ; Sir Thomas Lewis, F.R.S.,
and Dr. J. N. Douglas Smith for allowing me to
use their photographs for Plates, and Mr. H. F.
Witherby for much help and good advice.

Three of the photographs in this book were taken
by my friend W. G. H. D. Crouch, who was killed
in Bulgaria in the crash of Stamboul-Bukarest air
mail on 25th July 1931, just after he had arranged
for their inclusion. He served with me on the
Oxford University Greenland Expedition, and
although not strictly a bird-watcher, he had a
large part in shaping the theories and methods on
which this work is based. His steady resolution
and constructive realism are a bitter loss, and I
should like this book, which he helped to create
and to embellish, to be one of his memorials.

E. M. NICHOLSON.

LONDON, *4th September* 1931.

CONTENTS

9

CONTENTS

LIST OF ILLUSTRATIONS

PLATES

TEXT FIGURES

LIST OF ILLUSTRATIONS

CHAPTER I

EQUIPMENT

APPROACH TO BIRD-WATCHING

Approach to bird-watching—Trend towards organisation—Telescopes and binoculars—Note-books and note-taking—Books—Hides and observation posts—Trapping and ringing—Technique.

THE first significant fact about bird-watching is that one does not become a bird-watcher on purpose. Many of the neighbouring activities make a recognised career for men and women who pursue them, as botanists, ecologists and biologists of all kinds. Even those which count purely as sports, like shooting and fishing, are businesses with a long-standing organisation behind them and full provision for initiation of novices of all ages. But bird-watching remains, despite some excellent field clubs, on a much more haphazard footing. Its followers are not drawn from any one social class or type : they have nothing else in common with one another except the fact that they are bird-watchers, and if one attempts to investigate the more profound causes for this curious community of interest there is nothing more satisfactory to fall back on in order to explain it than the legal fiction of an Act of God.

Not only do people rarely become bird-watchers on purpose : in the past they have been liable to become bird-watchers in spite of themselves. Beginning with some such incompatible interest as shooting, or egg-collecting, or fishing they have come gradually under an influence which has forced them to desert their original path, and choose a new one altogether. In the future, perhaps, this will occur less often. We have now for the first time the possibility of recruiting bird-watchers directly and freely through the school natural history societies, Boy Scouts and similar movements, field clubs and by broadcast messages, instead of adopting at second-hand the recruits of related interests. The immediate approach has been considerably broadened, and such older transition stages as boyish egg-collecting, which meant so much for all but the newest generation of bird-watchers, are to some extent eliminated.

Most of the triumphs of bird-watching, and also most of its shortcomings, depend intimately on this haphazard approach. Its individualism, running often to childish secrecy and a chaotic absence of standards, its sturdy patience, its highly diversified and spontaneous genius coloured by a frequent naïvety of outlook, its daring departures from tradition and its absurd repetitions are all inseparable from this amateur and erratic basis. That must be recognised in order to appreciate the change which is already in full swing.

TREND TOWARDS ORGANISATION

The older bird-watcher was essentially an individual who might aspire to have at his finger-tips everything that there was to be known : the new bird-watcher is more frequently a member of some sort of organisation of observers concentrating on special questions, and renouncing any attempt at all-round knowledge. The older bird-watcher with a militant protestant outlook would seek to draw from each observation the most sweeping deductions not only about birds in general, but about Man and Nature and the works of God. The new bird-watcher adopts a more cautious and humble, and also a more scientific standpoint : the more he sees of wild birds the less knowledge he feels inclined to claim about them. In case it should be imagined that this humility is pure gain stress must be laid on the modern failure of initiative, springing largely from this source, which threatens to hinder every advance by demanding a leadership which it shows no sign of being able to provide. The effective contribution of bird-watching could be heavily multiplied if anyone could persuade even the existing bird-watchers of the many unsolved questions which it is within their power to solve. Ornithology tends to be held up because everyone grows so humble that no one comes forward to point out and undertake the work that urgently needs doing.

What is in fact happening in bird-watching is the inevitable development from an amateur and chaotic towards a professional and organised foundation characteristic of most civilised activities. The process may be regarded as either deplorable or welcome ; in any case it cannot be averted or denied. We even find traces of the steady mechanisation common to so many sciences and sports, although in bird-watching mechanical aids are restricted to fairly simple forms—field-glasses, cameras, hides, climbing and other approach devices, rings or bands, traps and a variety of experimental apparatus. Here, again, is a process which is going to transform bird-watching, whether we like it or not. With his television outfit set up in a Devon heronry or at a *lek* of blackcock in Northumberland the bird-watcher of the fairly near future may check, without leaving his house, or perhaps without leaving London, detailed observations painfully secured by isolated pioneers cramped, wet through, at dawn under flimsy canvas hides. It may be shocking that the acuter discomforts of bird-watching should be abolished for those able and willing to command increasingly intricate apparatus, but that undoubtedly is the way we are going. It is the same way, after all, that we have been going since the equally adventitious telescope and field-glass reduced the need for stalking by bringing birds closer to the observer.

It is no longer seriously open to us to discuss bird-watching in terms of the methods of even the recent past. Everything is already in the melting-pot : the new outlook, the new instruments and the new technique which are beginning to emerge promise or threaten (according to our point of view) an entire transformation during the coming years. We cannot stand sentimentally on the retention of inherited ways merely because we are used to them : on the other hand, in boldly adopting the new tools which are bringing so much more within the grasp of bird-watching, we must resist any tendency towards slavery to routine by setting against it the vital tradition of the older school.

We must keep bird-watching free from the jargon and pretence too liable to accompany a more developed technique : bird-watching can do with more method, but it can well do without more Methodology.

From these three foundations of bird-watching —instruments, technique and outlook—our discussion may conveniently begin. Having suggested how instruments tend to transform field ornithology the first business must be to explain more precisely what these instruments are.

The man who finds himself drawn towards some new field occupation naturally comes early to the question of equipment. There is, all the same, not a single piece of equipment that can be counted essential to the bird-watcher, in the sense that a rod is essential to the angler or a gun to the wildfowler. All the essential equipment of the real bird-watcher is inevitably inside him. Instruments are useful and often invaluable accessories, but they should never be more.

TELESCOPES AND BINOCULARS

Some form of optical apparatus for bringing birds closer to the observer than they actually are is probably the most consistently useful mechanical aid in bird-watching. Telescopes, binoculars and monoculars are the most common instruments for this purpose.

The telescope has very pronounced merits and disadvantages of its own. It gives easily higher magnification than any ordinary binoculars, and is relatively cheap. It has the further advantage of a good second-hand market, from the buyer's standpoint. But the drawbacks of the telescope are so serious that its use in bird-watching is inconsiderable, and tends if anything to decline. It is, to begin with, a long object much less portable than the binocular, whether slung over the back or carried among other gear. In use its high power and great extension call for something to rest it on, so that either a cumbersome tripod must be carried about with it or chance supports from trees, walls and so forth must be relied on wherever sustained watching is necessary. The high magnification usually involves in practice a considerably hazier definition than a good pair of field-glasses possesses. Finally birds are creatures peculiarly liable not to keep still, and for following fast-moving or flying objects the unwieldy telescope with its comparatively insignificant field compares very unfavourably with binoculars. The telescope, in fact, is an unsuitable instrument for all-round observation, although no doubt one can manage with it. Only in cases where both the station of the observer and the field of observation are more or less fixed—as in the intensive study of water-fowl on a lake from some commanding post, or the examination of a cliff breeding colony—is the telescope able to show superiority. Even then a pair of field-glasses for rapid spotting of points to investigate, or for following flying birds, is still a desirable auxiliary.

Binoculars of some sort are undoubtedly the most useful instruments of this type for the ordinary bird-watcher who works in a variety of different surroundings. They are compact, light, and portable, are commonly obtainable in powers well suited for bird-watching and are well adapted to the picking up of small objects against feature-less sky or water, or to intensive observation for many minutes or hours with little or no break, or to other special demands which the bird-watcher may have to make on them. But the term bin-oculars covers a wide range of objects, some of which are extremely valuable to the observer and others practically useless. It is highly important that they should be properly chosen ; they are things that have to be lived with for quite a long time.

There are two main types of binocular—the prismatic and the non-prismatic. Selection is simplified by rejecting all non-prismatic patterns straight away. Such patterns consist of a couple of parallel tubes which one looks directly through, like the common opera glass. Their magnification is usually negligible, and their field consists of two minute intersecting circles which are meant to show side by side, but frequently appear in practice one slightly above the level of the other. The only advantage of these instruments is that they are a little lighter and more compact than prismatic patterns and often a good deal cheaper. At any price they are not worth buying for bird-watching, though it is true that some elderly bird-watchers manage to use them. The prismatic type, which more seriously concerns us, has a characteristically angular form, due to its use of a series of mirrors. The construction is not simple, but it is certainly effective. With prismatic glasses you get the best combination of lightness, power, range of view and reliability available for observation at the present time. Your field consists, not of two small circles, but of a single large one. The stereoscopic effect is pronounced, and the definition of a really good pair of prismatic glasses has a very satisfying sharpness. Shaped to the hand, they may be held up for hours with only short breaks before the strain on arms or eyes becomes harsh. That, of course, presupposes a certain physique in the observer : it can only be said that first-rate prismatic glasses of suitable power do very much to minimise the strain of intensive bird-watching. Bird-watching without any strain is a contradiction in terms. The question of power is the one on which most room for intelligent disagreement certainly exists. It is an elementary mistake to imagine that in buying field-glasses for bird-watching the thing to do is to get the most powerful obtainable, or the most powerful that one can afford. High magnification costs more than mere money. It is bought at the expense of so many other desirable qualities that the question how far it is worth having needs careful weighing. For example, every increase of magnification brings a corresponding restriction of field and of light-transmitting capacity. This restriction is severe, the field at 1000 yards of a 6x glass being about 150 yards across, that of an 8x about 100 yards and that of a 12x only about 75 yards. There are Zeiss wide-angled glasses which cleverly counteract this restriction, but their price is naturally higher, while their light-transmitting capacity remains low. It might be supposed that the field at 1000 yards is a matter of importance only in looking at scenery, and that for focussing on particular birds the loss could well be put up with. To a certain extent that is true. The snag is in first picking out and then keeping focussed on your particular bird. Take the case where a bird settles in the upper branches of a tree in the middle of a wood. The bird-watcher with field-glasses magnifying only 6x has a good chance when he puts them up of picking out at once some salient branch or gap which will identify the part of the mass of foliage he is looking at and lead him rapidly to the spot where the bird is.

The man with 12x glasses on the other hand is likely to get an excellent highly magnified view of the foliage on such a scale that he ranges about seeking in vain some recognisable feature among the tangle. By the time he has got on to the spot where the bird came down seconds if not minutes have passed and the bird has probably disappeared. Against a sky or sea background the case is even worse. The field in which you have to look for your object is magnified just as much as the object itself, and where time is brief, as it is apt to be in the more exciting moments of bird-watching, any advantage accruing from the higher power

23

is more than offset by the delay in finding the object. There are further drawbacks as well. Bad light, for instance, means much worse strain for the user of high-powered glasses. Focussing is slower and more critical, and when the best focus is obtained it rarely has the same sharpness as that of an equally good instrument of less power : there is usually a suspicion of haze. Any unsteadiness either of hand, or through motion of a treetop observation post, or of a moving vehicle or boat is intensified to an unbearable extent as the magnification goes up. It is a debatable question whether the 12x field-glass can be fully used without a stand : 10x, and even 8x, suffer from the least vibration. (It is worth remarking, by the way, that people who value their eyes will avoid as far as possible the use of any sort of telescope or field-glasses from such positions as a moving train or car, or a motor launch with a definite " kick." Where binoculars have to be used in such circumstances the vibration can often be more or less neutralised for short periods by rising on tiptoe with flexed knees.)

It will be apparent from this discussion that I am a supporter of the prismatic field-glass magnifying 6x—which happens to be the most common tourist type. After using Goerz glasses of this description in an immense variety of climates and conditions, from a bird census in Greenland to night work from an observation post in the treetop zone of the South American rain-forest, I can only say that no pattern could have stood up better to hard treatment and exacting demands. All the same, it is arguable that the ideal all-round binocular for bird-watching may be a prismatic 8x, provided it is a really picked instrument. To be really safe, choose a 6x by a first-rate maker ; and some experienced persons who are by no means unpatriotic still consider that the best advice is to make sure by getting a Zeiss or Goerz. In buying field-glasses you have no check except the manufacturer's reputation on quality and durability. It is more than usually worth paying a higher price for a good one. Many cheap (and dear) instruments of French and British make are sold, most of which are not only unsatisfactory in definition or even in their register, but are quite unfitted to stand up to the very stringent treatment which a keen bird-watcher's glasses will certainly have to suffer. Since these main virtues cannot be tested by the inexpert, who must rely on the name, choice narrows down to certain minor points. Size and weight should obviously be the least possible without sacrifice in other directions. The case should be exceptionally tough, and the straps beyond suspicion as good leather. The question of eyepiece or rack focussing should not be over-looked. Some people like their focussing controlled by a central rack, others prefer each eyepiece to focus independently. Except for those comparatively rare persons whose eyes are both of equal strength eyepiece focussing has obvious advantages : if they use rack-focussing they have to have independent adjustment on one of the eyepieces which is a more cumbersome way of achieving the same result.

Moreover, the rack-focussing binocular is not dust- and water-proof to the same extent and is definitely a bad choice for tropical use, or trying climates generally. A leather rain-guard, at about 3s. 6d., is in any case a valuable extra protection, not merely against wet on the eyepieces, but against dust and scratches.

Certain more specialised instruments need bare mention. *The monocular* is one-half of a prismatic binocular sold independently. It is cheaper and of equal strength and definition : unlike the telescope it is also equally convenient to carry, use and focus, but it lacks stereoscopic field.

EQUIPMENT

Very high-powered binoculars with tripods are obtainable for special work, the best-known being the Ross Levista, which is made in powers of 16x and 25x. Periscopic binoculars, especially second-hand examples made for artillery work during the War, are often recommended for bird-watching, and in these the stereoscopic effect is exceptionally good, but they are very heavy and cumbersome for their power, which rarely exceeds 10 or 12x, and they can only be used with a stand or rest for long periods. " Donkeys' Ears " of this sort were used on the ornithological work of the Oxford University British Guiana Expedition, and proved on balance more trouble than they were worth. The fact that they are obviously useless for most ordinary purposes makes the optical salesman particularly eager to unload these khaki-tinted monsters at by no means a bargain price on any bird-watcher who falls into his toils, and it is worth thinking twice before accepting them. Taking Zeiss prices as a standard of the most that need be paid an ordinary 6x prismatic works out at about £9, an 8x at £10 and a wide-angle 8x from £11-£13. Second-hand glasses from a really sound firm are worth considering, but even second-hand binoculars are not really cheap without some very good reason for it.

NOTE-BOOKS AND NOTE-TAKING

The only article of equipment for bird-watching which can rank in importance with field-glasses, if not before them, is the note-book. But to explain what qualities should be looked for in note-books and where they are obtainable is probably superfluous. Any kind of note-book will do for bird-watching, although the sort with red covers are to be avoided, since they are apt to leave their mark on things if they get wet, and for the same reason pencil is more reliable than a fountain pen for leaving a written record.

The important point is not the note-book itself, but the manner of using it. Few, if any, bird-watchers make as much use of note-books as they might with advantage. Writing, especially in long-hand, is a slow business, and other claims on time are liable to curtail its allowance. In the field too scrupulous recording of things as they happen may result in the observer being caught unawares by some especially notable event occurring while he was busy describing a less important one : at home it is often hard to find enough time for transcribing fully the results of a full day. There is a persistent temptation to note down too little in the field, and leave too much till afterwards.

It is not nearly sufficiently realised what an important part may be played in the detailed understanding of bird life by putting down what is observed the minute after it has occurred. In a mere nature ramble, of course, where the observer notices the presence of a Whinchat and goes on to the next field to add a Woodlark to his day's bag, this immediate note-taking has no special merit. Where it does help is in watching a single individual, or a nest or a community, or some such continuous entity ; in fact in any sort of watching which is breaking fresh ground. Then it is found repeatedly that some scrap jotted down, perhaps half an hour or an hour earlier in the sequence of notes, is suddenly thrown into significance by something observed later. It is commonly reckoned that failure of memory only spoils observations left unrecorded for a day or a week, but actually the same process is at work on those unrecorded for half an hour.

It may be, and of course often is, desirable to scribble down in the field no more than will serve to recall for entry in permanent form what was seen. For any intensive work, however, a full field record with times and changing weather conditions and so forth is desirable. The permanent record should be either a loose-leaf book or a card-index, not a chronological diary, which will sooner or later grow unmanageable. Headings should be by species as a rule, but general headings for particular subjects of interest are often useful. Diagrams, sketches, and rough maps should be used as freely as possible : they often convey more than description, and with practice are more quickly made and read.

BOOKS

A more vexed question, which hardly arises in the field and yet goes to the root of all bird-watching, is the provision of books. No one, however expert, can get along without books, and since they are often fairly expensive items it is worth taking some trouble over finding the ones which will prove most useful. It has to be borne in mind that only a minority of the bird books published are of the slightest practical use. A great number of them might suitably bear the title *My Rambles among Birds*, since they are purely inconsequent narratives of what the author has seen, and often photographed, making no attempt to map out any ground and cover it properly. Several writers turn out books of this sort almost every year, even when they have already used the various chapters as separate magazine articles first. Bird books of this type may incidentally contain useful stuff on method or first-rate field observation, but they are rarely of permanent value and quite definitely are not worth buying except as extras to the working library which every bird-watcher needs. It is not necessary that this library should be expensive. It must include one or more accurate identification books covering the area in which he works, if possible a more local account of distribution, and then some books outlining bird-watching problems.

In England, for example, F. B. Kirkman's little *British Birds* (4th ed., 1928) in the " People's Books Series " is a first-rate identification book with descriptions of all the forms likely to be met with and many useful sketches, issued at 1s. 6d. Add H. F. Witherby's *Check-List of British Birds* (3s. 6d.) with its full list of names and status of every bird known to have been found wild within the British Isles, and the present writer's *Study of Birds* in Benn's sixpenny series, and you have a complete skeleton library of new up-to-date books for 5s. 6d. It is, of course, worth spending a good deal more, although access to any fairly complete library or museum will give almost all the reference backing that will be absolutely needed. In first taking up bird-watching the identification of birds met with remains for some time a recurrent difficulty. At this stage descriptions do not always help, and it is worth having, if possible, a fairly complete set of coloured plates. Works illustrated in this manner mostly cost a good deal—some in fact cost more than almost any other type of modern book—but for 25s. there is T. A. Coward's compact and informative *Birds of the British Isles*, in two volumes, with 455 coloured illustrations. This work, which is one of Warne's " Wayside and Woodland Series " is from the standpoint of the ordinary bird-watcher probably still the best worth getting : it came out in 1919-20, and a third volume of addenda, much less valuable, apart from its illustrations of many scarce forms, appeared in 1926. A more recent comparable work is F. B. Kirkman's and F. C. R. Jourdain's *British Birds* (21s., 1930). This omits all the rarer species, including some of by no means infrequent occurrence, and its descriptions are confined to salient features. Its information is accurate but rather sparse : it is however the most up-to-date work, and the best on habitat and call-notes. Another work to be considered in this class is Howard Saunders' *Manual of British Birds*, 3rd edition, revised and enlarged, by Dr. W. Eagle Clarke (25s., 1927).

The illustrations are archaic and poor, but the text covers fairly adequately all the birds on the British list.

The Practical Handbook of British Birds, edited by H. F. Witherby (2 vols., £4, 10s., 1919-24), stands in a class by itself as the standard work on the subject, but its minute feather descriptions in place of pictorial illustration limit its value for the bird-watcher. F. B. Kirkman's immense *British Bird Book* (1910-13) still contains the most complete treatment from the standpoint of field studies and life-history.

To pass to local and regional works most counties have been the subject of special ornithological compilations which are still obtainable either new, or more often second-hand. The majority are heavily out of date, and were never worth a great deal, but the ones dealing with the bird-watcher's particular field of operations are usually worth obtaining if they can be picked up at a reasonable price.

Places abroad are outside the immediate scope of this survey, but it may be mentioned that Wardlaw Ramsay's *Guide to the Birds of Europe and North Africa* (1923) is a pocketable and useful handbook as far as it goes, although not invariably accurate, and that W. B. Alexander's pocket

Birds of the Ocean (1928) covers every bird likely to be met with at sea (except as a vagrant) in any part of the world.

Identification books and local histories can only tell the bird-watcher what birds he is likely to meet, when and where he is likely to meet them, and how to recognise them when he does meet them. This is elementary. The class of books which discuss the living problems of bird-watching should be read by any observer who hopes to make a useful contribution to the subject that he has taken up. Of this class only a few examples can be named. Edmund Selous' *Realities of Bird Life* (1927) is of special value in presenting the journals of a veteran great bird-watcher in more or less the form that they were written in 'the field. H. Eliot Howard's *Introduction to the Study of Bird Behaviour* (42s., 1929) is of fundamental importance to the contemporary bird-watcher, and largely supersedes his earlier *Territory in Bird Life*, which is also worth reading. *Problems of Bird Migration* by Dr. A. Landsborough Thomson (1926) is a monumental survey of its subject, and of the bird-marking movement. *How Birds Live* (5s., 2nd edition, 1929) by the present writer discusses briefly many of the contemporary questions of bird-watching, including such subjects as the bird census, on which there is as yet no special work. Professor Julian Huxley's *Bird-Watching and Bird Behaviour* (5s., 1930) contains the broadcast talks with which he stimulated considerable interest in bird-watching during the spring of that year. Dr. Landsborough Thomson's *Birds* in " Home University Library " is a valuable essay.

Progress of observation and research is constantly making bird books out of date, even if they are not more or less out of date when they first appear. In order to keep touch with at least a part of current work it is advisable to subscribe to the magazine *British Birds* (yearly 20s.) which contains a number of papers, notes, and other communications on birds and matters of interest to bird-watchers. A growing number of regional reports appear in special areas, and these are usually worth the attention of observers working within their field, who can do much to increase their value by contributing notes on distribution and so forth.

It is necessary to add a warning against the misleading antiques which many second-hand booksellers try to dispose of at surprisingly high prices. It should be remembered that the nomenclature and often almost everything else in books above twenty years old is hopelessly obsolete, and that money may be frittered away in picking up supposed bargains which may be worse than useless. Old books should only be bought if they still serve some purpose better than later ones.

HIDES AND OBSERVATION POSTS

In the field the problem of hides and observation posts needs the consideration of a bird-watcher. The usefulness of these devices is precisely proportionate to the wariness and self-consciousness of birds under observation. Among Penguins or Greenland Ptarmigan, which are almost indifferent to human presence, its value may be very slight, while with exceptionally shy forms it may be essential for close-up work. The various methods of building hides have been so frequently explained by bird-photographers and lecturers that it is unnecessary to enlarge on the subject here. It is not advisable to lug about a very complicated and bulky, ready-made cabin ; some of the best and most effective hides are made almost entirely out of material available on the spot. A ground-sheet or large piece of canvas, of some dull green, brown or grey colour is useful for keeping out rain and as a support for any foliage, turves or mats of lichen or rushes laid on outside in order to

HIDE USED FOR BIRD-WATCHING AND PHOTOGRAPHING IN GREENLAND. OXFORD UNIVERSITY
GREENLAND EXPEDITION, 1928.

Photograph by W. G. H. P. Crouch.

harmonise with the surroundings. For support sticks about five feet long and strong enough to bear some weight can often be cut and pointed on the spot : as an alternative a strong collapsible tripod serves well enough. Comfort, space, ventilation and outlook are the chief problems of hide-using. The first can be solved on firm ground fairly accessible from a base by installing a light camp-stool with scope for change of position without wrecking the structure. Ventilation depends on circumstances : it is superfluous to point out that in sultry weather the interior of a cramped hide is liable to become distinctly stuffy, while the frequent conjunction of a plague of some sort of biting or stinging insects is also worth notice. In equatorial rain-forest at ground-level the increase of discomfort and perspiration inside a hide is particularly steep, and in such conditions failure to arrange adequate ventilation in advance may make the contrivance untenable. Finally there is the difficulty of securing a wide enough aperture to command all the movements of the subject of observation without raising suspicion. This, perhaps, is the one point at which a bird-watcher's hide problem differs from a nature-photographer's. The man with a camera focuses in advance on a place where he considers the bird likely to present his opportunity and disregards much that it does out of range, except so far as it bears on the prospects of a portrait. The bird-watcher, on the other hand, is interested in the bird's behaviour as a complete pattern, and therefore wants to see far more. In special cases—for instance at the foot of a cliff—natural obstacles may canalise a bird's movements within a narrow field of view : otherwise the best course seems to be to place the hide farther from the nest or other focusing point than a photographer must, with a correspondingly wider view, and to provide alternative peepholes commanding all directions which need only be opened as they are needed.

A special problem is presented by observation in high trees, which cannot be properly watched from ground level. On the Oxford University British Guiana Expedition, which aimed particularly at investigating the life of the treetop zone, this problem had to be faced in an acute form. The solution finally arrived at was dual. In two cases observation posts were established at 80 and 110 feet respectively above the ground, by a series of rope ladders lashed to forks, while in two more block-and-tackle was employed with triple-purchase rope for hauling up a light chair, with a back and arms but no legs, constructed of

38

packing-cases, forest timber for the frame, and bits of string, these two posts reaching 73 and 120 feet above ground. The advantage of a chair was its comparative comfort and simplicity of upkeep in an exacting climate : its chief drawback that the observer could only ascend with the aid of a team of two or three to haul him up, and needed at least one helper to get him down to earth again. Finally both systems were combined by the provision of equally comfortable hanging chairs at the top of the rope ladders, where they could be reached or left by a bird-watcher single-handed. The question of a hide was not tackled, the assumption being that treetop birds of un-inhabited bush would be too unfamiliar with the sight of a man to be easily alarmed by an observer suspended motionless at a hundred feet, more or less, above ground. This assumption was not wholly vindicated by experience : some sort of camouflage, provided it were sufficiently light and not too cramping, would be of service, especially with large wary birds such as Toucans and some Parrots, or small excitable ones like Humming-birds. As compared with a hide on the ground a treetop post has the disadvantage of comparative immobility. The time and exertion demanded for getting up a large tree and establishing a safe, comfortable observation post in it no doubt diminishes with practice, but is in any case considerable. Once fixed, the post may be raised or lowered, but there is no possibility of appreciable lateral removal if the site chosen proves unsatisfactory : in fact the only thing to do in that event is to cut the loss and begin on a fresh tree. It is therefore necessary to give much more care to preliminary survey before starting work on a tree-top observation post : the view it will command and the bird life visible from it must remain largely problematical until too late to change the plan. Where, as in Guiana, there are skilled native climbers available who will take a rope up anything in a remarkably short time this handicap is less serious than it must be where the choice lies between unpractised climbers and mechanical devices such as rocket apparatus and line-throwing guns, which, however efficient in themselves, are inherently unsuitable for the task of putting a rope over the one fork in a tangled canopy capable of giving safe purchase. In British woods, where trees do not grow 80 or 100 feet before the lowest fork, this difficulty is less severe, and a man of ordinary agility with climbing irons and some practice in using them can generally reach his objective. It is not, of course, practicable in

Fig.l.

Method of climbing trees by use of rope without swarming. A length of thin but
reliable climbing rope of about 100ft. is thrown over the first adequately strong
branch and jerked about until both ends are in the grasp. The ends are then
joined together with a knot and the entire rope, now forming a double strand, is
wound in a loose spiral round the trunk and made fast to any firm object within
reach on the ground, or if need be held by another person while the climber goes
up, holding one section of the rope in each hand and using his feet against the
trunk for leverage. The principle is similar to the well-known aboriginal method
of leaning backwards on a rope tied round the waist and jerked up foot by
foot, but it is applicable to English trees, which the aboriginal method is not,
since it depends on long climbs free from projecting limbs. The alternative of
swarming up the rope itself is less comfortable, even with a thicker rope, and
means trusting more heavily to the chosen branch, which there has been no
opportunity to test for safety.

ordinary circumstances to work an observation post reached by crude unaided climbing ; after the tree has once been conquered an easier permanent means of ascent must be created, with ropes or otherwise. The use of tall light observation towers must be considered in certain cases, and it is conceivable that given sufficient labour a long, cleared trail with a movable tower which could be shifted from point to point along it might justify experiment.

Movable hides deserve more attention than they have yet been given. The stalking-horse is an ancient conception, and an enterprising observer in California claims to have exploited successfully the stalking motor car. A moving car is of course a poor place for observation, and nothing could be less suitable than the modern low-roofed saloon : an antique open T-Model Ford surpasses it at every point. In Africa cars have been successfully used for approaching big game : a similar experiment in England is handicapped by the Road Traffic Act of 1930 which makes it a legal offence to drive more than fifteen yards off a road. Punts, canoes and rowing-boats are valuable where waterways give access. Where current, tide, or breeze is considerable the observer should have a companion to look after the craft.

Aircraft have potentialities which await exploitation, and in particular the silencing of airscrew and exhaust noise must enhance their value from this standpoint.

TRAPPING AND RINGING

In a future book on methods of bird-watching a description of trapping and ringing methods may require a place : at present it is impossible to include one, since too little has been done in this direction to give a basis for any sound indication. Trapping and ringing have developed too much as an isolated pursuit, and while it is clear that they must eventually dovetail into bird-watching at certain evident points the technique by which this is to be done remains to be adequately worked out. An account of the various forms of traps and of rings, with their advantages and disadvantages in practice, is of course outside the scope of this volume, and it is to be hoped that the lack of a full authoritative work on the subject will be remedied fairly soon.

TECHNIQUE

So far we have been concerned with a list of the instruments of bird-watching, from which it has emerged that instruments in use are either taken over more or less as they stand from other activities, or, to the extent that they are peculiar to the needs of bird-watching, remain at an elementary level of development. With this generalisation is bound up an evident corollary, that the technique of bird-watching is in an imperfect and fragmentary state. In fact a common technique applicable to problems as they occur is only just beginning to grow perceptible. As the discussion in the next chapter will show, most problems must still be tackled by *ad hoc* methods, whose effectiveness and elaboration varies greatly according to the re-source and intelligence exhibited by those who happen to have worked in any given field. It seems, all the same, safe to forecast that the coming period in bird-watching will see the recog-nition of a conscious integrated technique, super-seding with increasing rapidity the blundering methods of the past and even of the present.

The watertight compartments which have been allowed to be formed between, for example, ringers, bird ecologists, courtship and display students, workers on distribution and so forth, must dis-appear, although a form of specialisation will certainly survive and grow stronger. It is a ques-tion not only of technique, but of basic outlook.

After all, even the numerical organisation of bird-watchers shows large discrepancies between different places and different subjects, some working as isolated individuals, some as members of a society expressing their common interest, some as members of a disciplined team engaged in a predetermined plan. The present trend looks fatal to these casual differences ; methods and instruments as they are perfected must increasingly be exchanged between one group and another, and in the process bird-watching must acquire something like a common mind which it yet conspicuously lacks.

CHAPTER II

HOW BIRD-WATCHING IS DONE

Importance of selection—Use of books—Identification—Methods of observation—Investigating bird-song—Methods of recording bird-song—Watching the flock—Studying the individual—Ringing and trapping—Migration.

IMPORTANCE OF SELECTION

It is a frequent delusion that the bird-watcher is a man who rambles about the country-side until chance puts something in his way, like the common idea of a poet looking for inspiration. In fact waiting for something to turn up is no more to be recommended in bird-watching than in any other human pursuit. It is true that some make a habit of it, which largely accounts for the persisting myth that white Blackbirds' or Wrens' nests in cast-off human skulls are discoveries to get excited about. The real bird-watcher is not so poverty-stricken of ideas that he is forced to delve after these morbid and insignificant freaks. At its highest bird-watching is distinguished by an acute selectivity of object, and an unerring pursuit of it through a tangle of distracting clues. Compared

47

with the more intricate studies of birds in the field the triumphs of Sherlock Holmes look utterly childish. Contemporary bird-watching for example has been able not merely to show accurately how a Cuckoo deposits her egg, but to foretell just when and in what nest she is going to do it, so that the ornithologist can take up his station commanding the scene at a convenient moment before the event happens. The student of territory can predict to a yard how far the chase of a trespasser will be carried : the student of migration can tell almost to a day when the first Swallow or the first Wheatear will appear. That much remains incomprehensible is no proof that much is subject to chance, but more probably that we have yet to establish many of the principles behind bird life. To invade this field of the unknown is accordingly the ambition of bird-watchers : bird-watching becomes a sort of exploration which is just passing through its age of adventure.

The metaphor of exploration is worth lingering over. One does not go far in bird-watching any more than in exploring without energy and determination, a grain or two of robust common sense, and something to serve as a compass for finding the way. It is futile to wander round in circles or to tread slavishly along excessively beaten tracks: in order to accomplish anything one must strike out a definite line. Nor is it wise to persist in prospecting for non-existent gold in deserts when it means ignoring wells of oil or buried cities or dinosaurs' eggs which are lying waiting for someone to find them. The frequency with which bird-watchers overlook the subjects which they might brilliantly illuminate in order to repeat with mediocre results observations which have already been done over and over again is one of the more astonishing aspects of the art of bird-watching as practised up to the present time.

USE OF BOOKS

One of the less fortunate results of the deserved popularity of such classics as Gilbert White and W. H. Hudson is the rooted belief that bird-watching demands no special training, and that it is only necessary to go out and see what you can find in order to draw your own conclusions. Bird-watching, of course, has long passed this stage, and to take it up in such mystic faith is as absurd as to expect to become a crack shot without any shooting practice or to lay down the law on evolution without knowing any biology—as absurd, in fact, as both put together, for we started by

D 49

having to recognise that bird-watching is a sport and also a science, sharing the various difficulties which are the chief attraction of either. The first thing for a beginner at bird-watching to appreciate is accordingly that with all its crudities and imperfections bird-watching already has accumulated a rich fund of experience which is definitely worth drawing on. Obviously this fund may be drawn on in a number of ways : it may be tapped, for example, by reading some of the books in which it has partly been committed to paper, or by working with some seasoned bird-watcher who commands a good deal of it. Of these methods reading is the most universally available, and no amount of field experience can make up for the ignorance of bird literature exhibited by so many bird-watchers of considerable natural skill. The keen bird-watcher will devour every printed word about birds that he can find : in time he will discover a definite leaning towards certain subjects to the neglect of others—say, towards courtship, or migration, or a special group like the birds of prey. Such a bias should be cultivated ; its development will stimulate that reciprocal action between the inadequacy of what one reads and hears and the mystery of what one sees, which is the basis of all good field work. It is sound advice, then, to read the most and the best stuff on birds that you can get hold of, especially, of course, current scientific papers which describe the living problems of the moment. Among this catholic reading, if you are to be a bird-watcher, you will meet points which arouse your curiosity or disbelief and which can be put to the test among the species you are acquainted with in the field. Here is your starting point : take up the pursuit with energy and discretion, and you will be unlucky if you do not sooner enrich yourself, and perhaps also enrich the art of bird-watching.

IDENTIFICATION

Coming to the watching of birds in the field the first problem is to recognise which species they belong to. Bird-watching depends absolutely on correct sight identification. Without it you would have the same insuperable uncertainty which makes it almost impossible to record the habits of most insects reliably unless a specimen is secured at the same time. Field identifications vary in difficulty from the comparatively fool-proof Kingfisher, Pheasant or Magpie to the fine distinctions between Melodious and Icterine Warblers or Marsh and Willow Titmice which only a handful of observers can be reckoned competent to decide. Nevertheless, bird-watching has the great advantage that all British birds, unlike British mammals, fishes, insects or plants are definitely capable of being identified in the field. The same holds good, without serious exceptions, all over the world.

Identification books are still coloured by the tradition that what is demanded of them is a feather description for a corpse in the hand, and not a guide for field use. The satisfactory identification book for bird-watchers does not exist.

Much the best way of getting to know your birds in the first place is by going about with some fairly patient person who really knows them already. Failing that, frequent visits to a museum or familiarity with a good illustrated work will help considerably more than wading through too many involved verbal descriptions.

Identification is not just a matter of plumage and size : a good bird-watcher can give a correct determination without necessarily knowing either. If we analyse the factors by which species are expertly decided at a glance we get something like this :

(a) Build.
(b) Carriage, or action in flight, or both.
(c) Size.

(*d*) Plumage.

(*e*) Colour of " soft parts "—especially bill and feet.

(*f*) Song or call.

(*g*) Habitat and season.

(*h*) Other habits.

Such an analysis helps to make clear the inadequacy of the average identification book, even when it is well illustrated and accurate. (*a*) is sometimes, but not always, portrayed by the illustrations ; (*b*) only rarely ; (*c, d* and *e*) are more or less covered by plates and text ; (*f*) is never fully treated and often left out altogether ; (*g* and *h*) are better handled now than formerly, but still leave much to be desired. The order in which these items are given weight of course depends on circumstances. The present writer, although utterly ignorant of musical notation, prefers to rely on (*f*) wherever any sound is uttered, because almost every species can reliably be distinguished through its call or song by the trained ear. The value of familiarity with bird notes would be difficult for an observer to over-rate. In many more or less critical identifications—Marsh-tit and Willow-tit, Marsh-warbler and Reed-warbler, Skylark and Wood-lark, Meadow-pipit and Tree-pipit, Chiffchaff and

53

Willow-wren, Roseate Tern and Arctic or Common Tern, Carrion-crow and Rook, and several others— the call-note or song is instantly diagnostic at ranges when any sight identification is out of the question, or for that matter when the bird itself is invisible. Knowledge of call-notes enables one to keep track of migrants passing over in darkness— the familiar whisper of travelling Redwings heard on October nights is a good example. Even by day such high-flying species as Crossbills and Red-polls which might easily escape notice altogether are readily picked out and identified by their far-carrying characteristic notes. The bird-watcher, then, should lose no chance of improving his ear, remembering that an accurate recognition of calls and songs may be, and often is, quite independent of any talent or training in human music. It is a mistake, even where it can be done, to rely too much on special peculiarities of plumage. You should not identify House Martins by their having white rumps, but by their distinct fish-tailed shape, or their native lack of style in flying, or their language, or best by all of these. The bird-watcher who depends literally on a white mark here or a red bill there will find himself at a disadvantage every time he meets something outside the rule of thumb—for example an immature in a

strange plumage, or a related form. By learning to recognise birds on a broader basis one is better fortified against the unforeseen. Labels are useful, but they are not enough in themselves.

How far habitat and season should be used in identification demands brief discussion. To a certain extent they are used without question by all. For example, whenever we identify an Arctic Tern in this country we *assume* that the bird is an Arctic Tern after discriminating it from other British species, without attempting to prove that it is not a Swallow-tailed Tern (*Sterna vittata*, Gmel.) an almost indistinguishable species confined to the Southern Hemisphere. There is in the same way a fairly strong presumption against the presence of summer migrants in winter and *vice versa*, which ought to make the observer extremely careful, before reporting, say, a January Whinchat or a June Fieldfare, to make sure that there has been no confusion with the more probable Stonechat or Mistle-thrush.

No mistake is commoner or more discreditable to the man who makes it than this careless announcement of birds met with at highly improbable times or in very unlikely places. It is true that no record can be dismissed as out of the question ; the blunder is not to report an exceptional occurrence, but to report it quite casually, without

stating any grounds pointing to its genuineness, and often without appearing to appreciate how extraordinary it is.

Your credit as a bird-watcher must always depend on the fewness and plausibility of your errors of judgment. There is far too much disposition to make sweeping identifications on no valid evidence, which owe their correctness, if they prove correct, more to good luck than to good observation. So long as they are made in the heat of the moment and are not allowed to go on record hasty guesswork determinations are a pardonable luxury, although they rarely improve the plunger's reputation in the eyes of any competent bird-watcher who happens to accompany him in the field. Among a strange avifauna, where names are quite consciously tacked on as tentative labels, in lieu of the less memorable numbers favoured by botanists and entomologists, reckless sight identifications are more defensible ; generally speaking they must be counted among the worst offences which the bird-watcher can commit, and they are committed not simply by the impatient novice, but by the comparative expert who allows laziness or nervousness or vanity to get the better of his judgment.

If an unknown bird is seen the object must be to note as many points as possible which may tend

to identify it. That means that it must be approached or brought closer by field-glasses, enough to be examined in some detail. Birds flying over, or soaring, or perched in lofty foliage, or swimming at a distance present obvious problems, but the rule can always be observed of bringing the unidentified bird under the closest scrutiny possible. Then note its build, size, carriage and anything that will help to classify it ; scribble down a description of its plumage, colour of soft parts and an impression of its call or song if it utters any. Where it is seen, and what it does may help very materially ; also whether it is accompanying birds of the same or another species ; whether there is anything pointing to its being a resident or a wanderer, and so forth. Identifications are much helped by remembering the specific marks of the various families. One might, for instance, take down a minute description of a Tern which would fail to lead to identification if the colour of the bill were overlooked, or of a Gull if the colour of the legs were overlooked, while white foreheads, rumps, wing-bars or outer tail feathers, black caps, forked tails, crests and other salient marks are always worth noting first in dealing with unknown birds, since they so commonly turn out decisive. It must never be forgotten that any bird-watcher,

however expert, must leave a certain number of identifications uncertain; the man who can instantly give a name to every bird he sees is not an expert but a charlatan. All that anyone can do is to scrutinise the unknown for definite points which eliminate as many of the potential identifications as possible. If not enough can be made out to eliminate all potential identifications except one, or in other words to identify it, then the good observer must be content to leave it at that. It is important to realise that a doubtful record of a rare bird or unusual occurrence, if the evidence is well put, may do more for the reputation of the bird-watcher who makes it than a conclusive one more baldly stated. With familiarity all the birds more regularly met with will become instantly recognisable, so that the process of identification which looms so large before the beginner ceases to matter, or may in fact be performed unconsciously. But caution, thoroughness, and a respect for the demands of satisfactory proof can never be relinquished by the bird-watcher without bringing retribution.

METHODS OF OBSERVATION

In order to be of value, observation must be pointed. There are persons who spend their

leisure dashing from one sanctuary or haunt of
rare species to another, bagging fresh experiences.
Such persons can scarcely rank as bird-watchers.
Although less destructively inclined they are
essentially as childish as unscientific egg-collectors,
or perhaps, better still, as autograph-hunters or
stamp-collectors. They collect memories, but they
differ from the æsthetic bird-watchers like W. H.
Hudson in that the memories they are concerned
with owe their value, not to any transcendent impression of beauty, but primarily to the fact that
their subjects happen to be uncommon birds.
Whether bird-watching is embraced æsthetically
or scientifically, or even as a sport, this restless,
superficial flitting from one object to the next in
the spirit of going on to yet another night club is
totally destructive of a real enjoyment.

Such an attitude betrays ignorance of the
complexity and profundity of any aspect of
bird life which is carefully considered. There
is nothing to which you can turn which does
not bristle with unanswered questions. In order
to give some idea of the possibilities of pointed
observation it may be well to discuss two or
three problems in some detail.

INVESTIGATING BIRD-SONG

Take first of all the subject of bird-song, which many observers in this country have opportunities for investigating. For whatever species may be selected it should be ascertained about what dates the song-period normally begins and ends. Do these dates vary much from year to year? Does the volume of song within the song-period change or fluctuate considerably? If so, when is the real peak? Is this peak affected by weather, or is it fixed and constant? Is there a steady rise in song-volume towards the peak and a steady fall afterwards, or are there other smaller peaks? If one distinguishes mated cocks from unmated ones, what contrasts, if any, emerge over the song-period? Is the song fairly rigidly confined to a definite season, or does it occur sporadically in other months? Does the song begin before dawn, or continue after dusk, or at night? Does it increase or decline in volume at certain hours, or is it fairly continuous throughout the day? Can any such fluctuations be attributed to heat or any other external factor? Is the song of an even quality throughout the song-period? Does it appear to start perfect or is perfection only attained after some practice at the beginning of the season? Is there any notable change or deterioration later ? How far does the song carry ordinarily and in extreme cases ? Has it a thoroughly stereotyped form, or is it rambling and improvised ? Does it contain imitations of other sounds, songs or calls ? Are there alternative versions of the song ? Does the song vary perceptibly in different regions ?

What traces of sub-song or inward whispering notes can be detected at close range ? Is the sub-song similar to the true song, or more extensive, or different ? Does it contain notes or phrases reminiscent of related or other species ? Is the sub-song uttered from a hidden or a conspicuous perch ? At what dates is it noted ? Is it in any way confined to immature birds, or to those in imperfect voice, or in process of moult ? Do both sexes utter the song or sub-song, or both ? Is song delivered from a prominent perch ? Is there a regular singing-stand, or series of stands, or is any suitable perch used haphazard ? Is song uttered from the ground ? If so, is its quality unaffected ? Is singing on the wing normal ? If so, is it accompanied by any characteristic or peculiar song-flight ? Are there specific mannerisms which go with the song ?

What relation does song bear to reproduction ? Is song or sub-song observed in migrants on passage or in winter quarters ? If so is it in any way distinguishable from song in the breeding season ? Does the song-period begin before, during, or after mating ? Does either true song or sub-song bear a major part in courtship ? How does song link up with territory ? What is the reaction of other males to the singer ? If he is on the move, do they persecute him ? Are they stimulated to sing against him ? Where separate territories are held, are they drawn towards or across the singer's boundary ? Does fighting follow, and in this case is the song interrupted or given up ? How do the hens, mated or unmated, seem to react to it ? Where separate territories are not held what effect does the song have on others ? Is song delivered from near the nest ? Is it within hearing of the nest ? Does it cease or change after the eggs are laid or hatched ? If it continues after the fledging of the young, how do the young react to it ?

It is clear from this barrage of questions, which could easily be extended, that scrutiny of any single point in bird-watching exposes an intricate set of problems many of which are unsolved for any species in the world, and all of which are unsolved for most species. Confronted with this complex mystery how is one to proceed ? Evidently some skill and pertinacity are demanded, and such moral or mental qualities must be taken for granted ; here it is a question purely of material weapons and methods. Suppose it is decided to investigate bird-song. The best plan will be to use a good-sized loose-leaf note-book, to be kept on a dual species and subject basis. First a sheet or sheets will be set aside for every songster covered by the investigation, others being added as required from time to time. Every observation touching a given species will be entered under it, or referred to if entered elsewhere. The old-fashioned way would be to enter, say :

8th February.—Chaffinch first sings. Sunny.
9th   ,,   Several in song. Mild.
10th   ,,   None heard. Cold and rainy.

In practice this method involves a mass of unnecessary writing, and much essential negative evidence is probably not kept. For any day-to-day routine notes a graph or diagrammatic form is much simpler and more useful. In the accompanying figure (Fig. 2) a large disc-shaped diagram divided radially into twelve equal parts representing the months enables not only the duration of the song-period but the approximate volume of song from time to time to be recorded with considerable accuracy without any writing at all. This system has the further advantage that the duration and volume of song in any given species can be compared at a glance with those for any other of which similar data are kept, the contrasts between such closely related forms as Blackcap and Garden-warbler, Robin and Nightingale, or Blackbird, Throstle and Mistle-thrush being far more illuminating than any verbal account. As far as duration is concerned the system is fool-proof so long as observation is regular and at the same place. For volume the best method of securing comparable results is to estimate the number of utterances per hour in terms of the highest intensity observed at the peak of the season. Thus if (to take a simple hypothetical case) there are ten males of a given species on the area observed and they sing, at the height of the song-period, on an average forty times each per hour, then that may be taken as the basic 100 per cent., so that when it is estimated later that out of eight males still present four have ceased singing and the other four are averaging about ten times per hour, the general average song-volume will be taken as $12\frac{1}{2}$ per cent.—*i.e.*, five times per hour for all present. Any attempt to evolve a basic standard

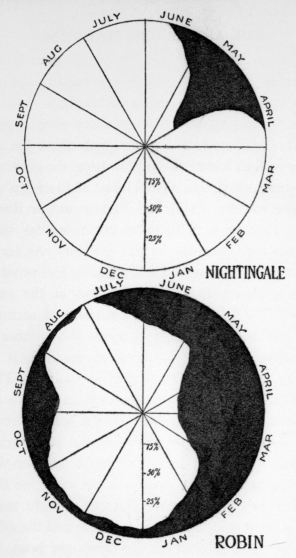

NIGHTINGALE

ROBIN

Fig.2. Diagrams showing method of
recording period and intensity of song by
species on discs divided into 12 sectors
representing months of the year. _The
cases_ _given_ _are_ _hypothetical_, _not
being_ _based_ _on_ _data_ _actually_ _obtained._

common to all species will probably fail, but diagrams based on a mere estimate of volume, like wind-forces on the Beaufort scale, will be quite valuable so long as the estimates are carefully made with a constant standard in mind, which is adequately explained in publishing results based on it.

METHODS OF RECORDING BIRD-SONG

The difficulty of arriving at any scientific method of recording bird-song is one of the main reasons why knowledge of the subject is in such a backward state. Certain pioneers attempted to use musical notation, but it is now generally admitted that except for a very few species musical notation will not serve. The average writer has confined his attention to more or less unusual songs and notes, which he has tried to compare to other sounds, usually of a mechanical sort which might or might not give the reader some idea what they were like. The best descriptions of this sort are such well-known comparisons as that of the Corn-bunting's song to the jangling of a bunch of keys, or the Common Snipe's drumming to the bleating of a goat ; the worst of them amply justify the humorist's nature note on the Red-eared Crested Jape whose song sounds

" like a box falling on a lighthouse, but not so frequently."

The alternative to musical notation or comparison with known sounds—and many of the sounds most familiar to one generation are barely a memory to the next—is some form of phonetic imitation. In its crude shape, as *"Wet-my-lips"* or *" A little bit of bread and no che-e-ese,"* this method has long been familiar, but the effort to make something like an adequate instrument out of it has only lately begun. Mr. W. Rowan's solution, described in *British Birds* (Vol. XVIII, p. 17, 1924) is probably the most satisfactory yet achieved. The basis of it consists of the four symbols :

U for a very brief note without particular accent.
⌣ for a longer note without particular accent.
— for a short note well accented.
— for a longer note well accented.

Continuity is represented by a thin bowed line, and beneath the symbols comes a phonetic rendering of the call. Finally the relative pitch of the various notes is indicated by dropping or raising each syllable above the one before it, varying the length of drop to suit each case.

Mr. Rowan accordingly represents the varying call of the Cuckoo as :

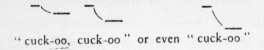

" cuck-oo, cuck-oo " or even " cuck-oo "

He points out that the call late in the season may become either—

" cuck-cuck-oo "   or   " cuck-cuck-oo,"

a contrast not reproduced in cruder forms of representation. Further possible elaborations include < to indicate a swell as in the Wood-warbler's trill or ⌐ to indicate slurring of the note as in the Curlew's   Mr. Rowan's method has

" cur-ee."

proved highly practical, and bird-watchers should certainly try to follow it wherever song or call-notes have to be recorded. A wider adoption of this technique would do much to liquidate the present ignorance and confusion about the language of even our commonest birds.

Given some appreciation of the problems involved in bird-song, a field of observation in which at least one singing species can be well studied and a technique for recording the form,

69

duration and volume of song met with, the prospects of valuable and absorbing work are evidently good. By keeping notes under such headings as " Song and Territory," " Imitation in Song," or " Effects of Weather " as well as under species titles significant observations will be grouped together in such a way as to throw light on parts of the subject, while at the same time raising fresh questions in others. Of course, everything in bird-watching is infinite ; there is no possibility of exhausting the unknown, but only of limiting it.

WATCHING THE FLOCK

To sketch another rather different field for bird-watching the flock may be taken as an example. The unanswered questions about flocks are as numerous and fundamental as those touching bird-song. Does the flock remain permanently in being ? If not, does it disperse for the breeding season, or at other seasons ? Does it assemble every night for common roosting, or daily for common foraging, or merely occasionally for such functions as courtship, migration or play ? Is it quartered permanently on the same area, or does it wander or migrate outside it ? Does it travel as a compact unit in high purposive flight, or does it move in a straggling troop ? What guides the flock in its movements ? Does it follow woods, hedges, valleys or the course of rivers ? Is it led by a single individual, or is the leading position constantly changing hands ? Do movements occur instantly in unison, or does the flock hesitate between two or more directions ? Does it ever split and re-unite, or remain divided ? Is any contact note or signal used to keep touch, especially in darkness or among foliage ? Is there any perceptible signal given for a change of direction ? Does it follow a definite beat, daily or periodic ? Is it composed of a number of mated pairs, or of one sex only, or of non-breeding adults, or of immatures, or of some mixture of these ? Is courtship or other sexual activity noticeable, or is the flock virtually sexless ? In case of flocks formed only for the winter how far does the process of mating and finding territory go before the flock disintegrates ? Does the strength fluctuate at different hours or seasons, and if so, why ? Are other birds of the species forming the flock present locally without adhering to it ? If so, are they in flocks of their own, or as scattered individuals ? Where flocks of non-breeding birds of territorial species remain in being through the breeding season what are their relations with the breeding pairs on territory in the neighbourhood ? Do they respect territory, or avoid it, or ignore it ? What are the relations of the flock to other birds of the species forming it, or to related and unrelated forms ? What advantages seem to accrue from membership of the flock ? Is it in any way aggressive against competitors or birds of prey ? Is there appreciably greater security against enemies ? Is there any commensal advantage comparable to the advantage of a large shooting party with beaters over a single man with a gun ? How does the flock arise ? Is it apparently a clan of blood relations ? Is it a snowball aggregation of individuals or parties which have happened to coalesce ? In the case of mixed flocks, which species are usually dominant, and why ? From how many species are they drawn ? Do all members of the species concerned always join a mixed flock where one is available, or do some prefer independence ? How far are the various species concerned competitive over diet ?

Such questions show that the problem of flocks, which every bird-watcher has to meet in one form or another, is far from simple.

While serving as ornithologist on the Oxford University British Guiana Expedition of 1929 the present writer had to deal with this problem in one of its most acute forms. The tropical rain-forest of South America is made particularly difficult for observation by the fact that its treetop zone, rising to a maximum of just over 150 feet above the ground monopolises most of the light, and condemns the ordinary observer to wander on foot in semi-darkness through more or less dense bush in touch only with the more terrestrial members of its mixed flocks. These flocks have clear horizontal divisions, some species belonging purely to the treetops, others to the high trunks and hanging bush-ropes, others to the lower strata of foliage, and others to ground-level. Their observation was accordingly handicapped. It was undertaken with a high degree of success by or-ganised attack from several angles. Paths or " lines " were cut on a concentric system, con-nected with base-camp by a series of radial arteries. These served not only for rapid and silent move-ment, like the gamekeepers' " rides " through an English wood, but also as the basis of a fairly accurate sketch-map. Previously, even where the bush was open enough for free movement the task of not getting lost made considerable distractions, and it was out of the question accurately to re-construct the devious route of a mixed flock. With the aid of the path system and the map these difficulties vanished. On falling in with a mixed flock it became possible to follow it for hours, marking on a prepared map the time at which it crossed each path and gave a check on its position. By this means it was shown that the first impression of these flocks being either migratory or engaged in wide wandering was quite mistaken ; on the contrary they circulated in elliptical orbits or figures-of-eight within a remarkably confined area, occasionally doubling back on their tracks when a strong element of their highly sedentary membership found itself as far afield as it was prepared to go (see Fig. 3). These conclusions were confirmed from four observation posts at heights between 60 to 120 feet above ground at selected points above the path system, from which the track and composition of the mixed flocks could comfortably be overlooked. No doubt this case involved more spadework and organisation than the ordinary bird-watcher would be able or ready to undertake. Normally, however, the difficulties which call for them are not found. In England the map basis is usually available to hand, while the trees are not lofty enough to require observation posts in their crowns. But the value of mapping as a weapon in bird-watching remains constant everywhere. It is by no means

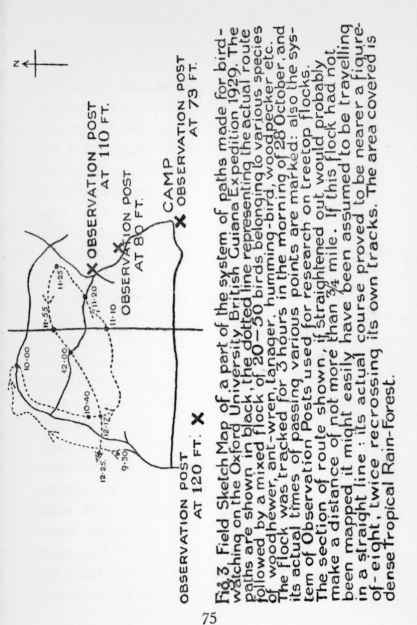

Fig.3 Field Sketch Map of a part of the system of paths made for bird-watching on the Oxford University British Guiana Expedition 1929. The paths are shown in black, the dotted line representing the actual route followed by a mixed flock of 20–50 birds belonging to various species of woodhewer, ant-wren, tanager, humming-bird, woodpecker etc. The Flock was tracked for 3 hours in the morning of 28 October, and its actual times of passing various points are marked: also the system of Observation Posts used for research on treetop flocks. The section of route shown, if straightened out would probably make a distance of not more than 3/4 mile. If this flock had not been assumed to be travelling in a straight line: its actual course proved to be nearer a figure-of-eight, twice recrossing its own tracks. The area covered is dense Tropical Rain-Forest.

75

understood how many mysteries dissolve when one attacks them by putting down the data on a sketch-map as one goes along. The bird census in particular relies very largely on map work. Whether it is a question of counting a large heronry or rookery or dealing with the bird population of a district or country the map is indispensable. But it is indispensable also for working out individual territory, for studying migration routes, for distribution and for much else. The magic virtue of the map depends largely on the fact *that* it has comparatively little bias. In conventional observation the subjective element is apt to be too strong. The bird-watcher sees what he is looking for, but is curiously blind to what lies outside his preconceived ideas. In mapping this subjectivity tends to disappear. Mathematically the map demands filling in, and in demanding it repeatedly opens the eyes to clues which had escaped them.

STUDYING THE INDIVIDUAL

Until very recently birds were regarded usually from the standpoint of that convenient myth, the species. It was stated, for example, that the Cuckoo was promiscuous or polyandrous, that the Little Owl was beneficent and so forth. Whatever an individual bird was seen to do once its species was taken to do habitually. Modern bird-watching has done much to correct this crude and flat view of the subject. In some ways, as this book has already suggested, birds possess so little liberty of action that it is possible to forecast with remarkable accuracy how they will respond to a given stimulus. Most of the supposed cases of a high avian intelligence have not borne examination. Nevertheless, the individual bird definitely is an individual, and not an automaton. He is worth getting to know. As yet we have scarcely begun to know him.

Keeping track of the individual seems much harder than it really is. On a superficial glance all of a species look alike. When one encounters the same birds day after day idiosyncrasies and points of recognition begin to leap to the eye, especially with the larger forms. An infallible method of fixing identity, where it can be practised, is to trap the birds to be watched and mark them with a coloured ring plainly visible in the field. Attempts have occasionally been made to stain the plumage conspicuously in order to identify specific birds for intensive observation. Mr. John B. Price used with success artist's oil colours dissolved in carbon-tetrachloride for applying to the light feathers of the head and neck of California Quail (*Lophortyx californica*) which he studied during 1927-29 on the campus of Stanford University, U.S.A.[1] He records that the other Quail did not persecute the stained ones in any way, and that the colour could be distinguished for a month and a half, and in one case as much as seventy-four days. In British climatic conditions the period would probably be much shorter. The number of distinctive tints available is another severe limitation. In the case above quoted the stain was applied by flocks, sixty-five members of one flock being stained orange, thirty-four of another yellow and forty-four of a third red. The greater permanence of coloured rings and the greater number of recognisable marks possible through them evidently constitute advantages which will not easily be neutralised.

Having once marked a number of birds by use of traps a field of investigation has been entered which is still so unknown that almost anything encountered in it is likely to be of value. It becomes a question of seeking out the subjects of the study from day to day, finding out whether they stay about the same place, or are liable to

[1] *Some Flocking Habits of the California Quail*, by J. B. Price. Condor, XXXIII. pp. 3-7, 1931.

vanish and reappear after an interval, or not to reappear at all. With the breeding season the mate and young should if possible be clearly marked, with a view to discovering whether mating is for life, or for a season or two, or only for part of a season, and whether there is inbreeding. A pedigree, however incomplete, of some sedentary species in a wild state over several generations would be of the utmost value.

The pioneer studies of Mr. J. P. Burkitt, whose papers on the British Robin appeared in *British Birds* (Vol. XVII, pp. 294-303; XVIII, pp. 97-103 and 250-257; and XIX, pp. 120-124) have indicated what might be done in this country by such intimate observation, but this lead remains to be adequately followed up.

RINGING AND TRAPPING

While marking of individual birds in order to make them recognisable in the field is rarely attempted the use of numbered rings which can only be checked on recapture or death is practised on a large scale over most of Europe and North America. The *British Birds* scheme directed by Mr. H. F. Witherby has accounted for more than 300,000 birds since 1909, and is now (1931) in-

creasing the total at a rate of nearly 30,000 yearly.
Rings are made in five sizes, ranging from a
specially light type designed for the smallest birds
to a bulky band secured by a clasp for use on Cormorants or Herons. Each carries the inscription
WITHERBY, HIGH HOLBORN, LONDON, and a serial
number stamped on the light aluminium compound
which identifies the particular bird on which it is
found. Rings are sent out in packets to the
ringers, who are kept informed of progress through
the periodical *British Birds*. The packets are
accompanied by blank schedules, to be filled in as
the rings are used with details of the number, date,
species, locality and name of marker, and where
possible the age (adult, immature or nestling) and
sex of the marked bird. In case of young birds
those belonging to a single brood are linked together. When a recovery is made the ring number
alone is sufficient to identify the record, for no
number is repeated. Each autumn the schedules
are called in, together with a list of birds marked
in the foregoing season. The totals are then made
up and the schedules cut into separate card entries
to be filed and to await recovery notifications.

Bird-marking began on a chance basis, and it
was for some time believed that the ambition must
be to ring as many birds as possible in the hope

that enough of them would be heard of sooner or later to make the undertaking worth while. This hope was not disappointed, but it gradually became clear that the return varied constantly and to a great extent in different parts of the field. Generally speaking, where trapping was practised recovery percentages were high. Where birds were marked in the nest the results were not nearly so good, except with birds of prey, game or wild-fowl and a few other species heavily shot as vermin. For small migrants, such as the Warblers, and oceanic birds the work proved especially unremunerative. The tendency has therefore been, as the number of ringed birds has increased, to restrict the field to the more profitable forms. In March 1931 the revised instructions to *British Birds* ringers put a veto on marking nestling House-sparrows, Goldcrests, Tits, Skylarks, Willow-warblers, White-throats, Spotted Flycatchers, Wrens, Sand-martins and Black-headed Gulls. In response to appeals from trappers, who had lately begun to play an important part in the British marking scheme, the former veto on certain adult birds was removed, except for the obvious reservation that Pheasants, Partridges and Grouse of any age might not be ringed.

The old-fashioned ringer who did the rounds of

the hedgerows compiling huge totals by marking
large numbers of nestlings of sedentary forms has
been given a definite check. Ringing, like everything else in field ornithology, becomes selective
instead of promiscuous. Work must in future be
concentrated on two fields—the intensive marking,
as nestlings, of species formerly neglected or
exceptionally remunerative in returns, and the
intensive development of trapping. The connection of the first field with bird-watching is
slender. Occasionally a ring found in a Hawk,
Owl or Raven casting may establish the identity
of some unsuspected victim, but generally speaking
ringing of nestlings is an act of faith which, if it
fructifies, will probably do so through some remote
person whom the ringer has never seen. Trapping,
which may be taken to include the fairly frequent
practice of catching birds on the nest, is on a
different footing. It can be used with success
in connection with a variety of bird-watching
problems. The age to which birds live, and the
company they keep are obvious points on which
trapping can yield invaluable data. The fact that
certain birds easily acquire the trap habit, coming
back repeatedly, sometimes two or three times on
the same day, gives opportunities for experiment
which have hardly begun to be exploited. Since

83

the early spring of 1928 the Oxford Ornithological Society has carried out a certain number of experiments on the homing ability of Greenfinches, which have resulted in retrapping after a very short interval of birds taken out by car to distances of up to six to nine miles in various directions and then released.

Work of this sort is bound to develop as its potentialities become better understood. It is axiomatic that natural laws are best elucidated by tampering with their working. Generations of concentrated study of the times and routes and distances of bird migration have brought us remarkably little nearer to understanding any of the fundamental problems involved. A decisive advance cannot occur purely through old-fashioned straightforward bird-watching; it must depend largely on experiment. Three lines of experiment have already been begun and found fruitful. In the first direction J. B. Watson and K. S. Lashley, by catching Noddy and Sooty Terns on the nest on Florida Keys and removing them to distances of several hundred miles, established their ability to return to breeding quarters from areas of featureless ocean over which they could hardly have had any external guide, since the species does not range up to the latitude in which they

(*Upper*) TRAP USED FOR RINGING NEAR CARLISLE
Photograph by Dr. J. N. Douglas Smith.
(*Lower*) HOUSE-TRAP USED BY THE OXFORD ORNITHOLOGICAL
SOCIETY
Photograph by W. G. H. D. Crouch.

were released. In a small way this exciting work has been followed up by such experiments as those at Oxford above mentioned, and there is no reason to doubt that the recovery or non-recovery of wild birds marked and transported to a distance by methods excluding any possibility of their observing the route taken will greatly illuminate the mystery of homing ability. Among the tasks which suggest themselves are :

(*a*) Transporting birds which have acquired the trap habit to a gradually increasing distance from the trap after each recovery, in order to establish whether there is a definite area which they know, and outside which they tend to get lost.

(*b*) Rearing young of the same species in captivity and releasing them at a distance in similar circumstances in order to discover what differences, if any, occur in their behaviour.

(*c*) Tests designed to bring out any differences of response between residents and migrants.

On a second line of experiment Thienemann, by detaining German White Storks until after their usual migration date in autumn, has found indications that the migratory impulse is of very limited duration, and that birds unable to obey it at the right time are hopelessly confused in their response when released afterwards.

In the third direction Rowan, in Canada, has shown by experiment that birds of comparatively delicate species possess, in fact, great resistance to cold and exposure so long as they are well fed in an outdoor aviary, and has proceeded in a series of bold but complex experiments which only a trained biologist could undertake to probe the roots of the migratory impulse. His work cannot be described, but in any migration study reference should be made to his paper.[1] He finds, like Thienemann, that detained migrants released in mid-winter behave abnormally, and may fail to migrate even under pressure of starvation.

Even if no experiments with trapped birds are attempted the mere routine of trapping will expose many unsuspected problems—for it is one of the chief attractions of all forms of bird-watching that the result is more frequently to expose fresh problems than to clear up the ones whose solution was originally aimed at. Each successive recapture helps to fill in the biography of the bird in question

[1] "On Photoperiodism, Reproductive Periodicity, and the Annual Migrations of Birds and certain Fishes," by W. Rowan, *Proc. Boston Society Nat. Hist.*, 1926, 38 pp., 147-189.

by giving, sometimes over several years, a series of fixed points in his career.

MIGRATION

The study of migration was formerly one of the most emphasised of all bird-watching problems. With the development of ringing, trapping and experimental technique it has taken on a new shape. Direct observation may establish with difficulty on which coasts migrants arrive or depart, and may locate fairly accurately the winter and summer quarters, but exact information on the travels of particular birds can only be got through ringing. In the same way the trapping experiments already mentioned obviously supersede the blundering speculations of the detached observer. Into these fresh channels the main effort to clear up the migration problem has recently flowed. The venerable tradition of watching eagerly for the first appearance of the various migrants, and for indications of their route and method of travel, has not lapsed but it tends increasingly to be carried on by amateur and often unintelligent observers. The great co-operative inquiries which found data for the British Association and British Ornithologists' Club reports of the pre-war period have fallen into unpopularity. Only on such favoured coasts as those of Norfolk and Fair Isle does migration still excite something like the old enthusiasm.

Must it be concluded then, that migration offers no more scope for the ordinary bird-watcher? Quite certainly migration is one of the more dangerous subjects to take up. Unlike almost any other problem of bird-watching it can rarely be profitably investigated except on a grand scale. Courtship, territory, the rearing of young, bird-mind, special adaptation and even such matters as population can be tackled in miniature, but to observe migration one needs an army. Since the rival techniques of ringing and trapping were developed the incentive to raise armies for this particular campaign has declined. It is true that in the autumn of 1930 the sanguine head of the German Ornithological Observatory on Heligoland undertook to make simultaneous observations of passage by means of a line of observers posted all round the North Sea from Norway and Denmark through Germany, Holland and Belgium to the Straits of Dover and up the east coast of Great Britain to the northern isles. But the response, although not weak, showed clearly how far the more active minds in bird-watching had moved from this particular ambition. In fact visual observation of passage is fatally compromised by the fact that the observer's station, whether a ship, lighthouse or point of land, so frequently diverts the migrant from its original course before it is observed. While Dr. Drost was probably right in holding that no smaller theatre than the entire North Sea basin would serve the purpose of a simultaneous survey of migration in progress, it is clear that a high proportion of the population of all the countries concerned would have to be trained bird-watchers, and to take part in the scheme in order to give a human net so close that nothing important could escape it. Moreover, ships would have to be stationed at mathematical intervals all over the North Sea to check the migrants intermediately. In other words, such a scheme could only be counted practicable provided that it is carried out so sketchily that any accurate result is out of the question.

The recording of special waves of migration, and of the dates of arrival of the various migratory species is clearly within the scope of the bird-watcher, but the data on these subjects are rather too abundant than too scarce, and amassing more, except with some definite plan for extracting significance from them is not to be encouraged. In fact, it has to be recognised that the initiative has passed, at least for the moment, to the ringer and experimenter. The simple bird-watcher has little useful to do with migration, except in remote or neglected regions, unless he is content to follow up the new lines of attack which are thus opened for him.

He may, for example, look for evidence of the northward drift in late summer which many migrants, and especially their young, are shown to undertake in this country between their breeding season and their southward journey. He may investigate the dispersion of oceanic birds which leads to such curious recoveries as the series of transatlantic Kittiwake journeys or those of British marked Puffins, Guillemots and Razorbills to Scandinavian waters. But migration, at any rate for the present, is not to be advised as a special study except to the bird-watcher with uncommon opportunities.

CHAPTER III

THE BIRD CENSUS WORK

BIRD NUMBERS

BIRD-WATCHING is impelled not only by an ambition to diminish the field of the unknown but by
the need for continual revision, in the light of more
searching standards, of what is taken for granted.
One of the more conspicuous instances at the
moment is the revulsion against the looseness of
such terms as " rare," " common," and " abundant " which have been applied so light-heartedly
in the past with an entire absence of consideration
for any criterion beyond the momentary impression of the observer using them. It has become
only too obvious that the same species in the same
area might be ranked very differently by different
observers, and that the discrepancies would refer,

not to any variation in the strength of the species, but to variations in the competence, opportunities, or temperament of the observers. This subjective element must clearly be weeded out, if bird-watching is to claim any scientific validity. The search for a universal and reasonably stable standard gradient of numbers has accordingly been taken up with enthusiasm during the past thirty years from Berlin and Oxford to California. Up till the middle of the twentieth century at least it seems likely to remain one of the most pressing interests of ornithology.

Whatever approach is favoured, and there have been many, the invariable tendency of this demand is to stimulate census work. The bird census may be considered under four main headings, according to type :

(*a*) Complete individual census.
(*b*) Sectional census.
(*c*) Census by sample.
(*d*) Specific census.

(*a*) COMPLETE INDIVIDUAL CENSUS

Complete individual census is clearly the most adequate method, but its very exhaustiveness has the effect of confining it to small areas. If you are to count every individual bird with any pretence at accuracy the amount of ground you can cover must obviously be pretty limited. In Greenland, on the Oxford University Expedition of 1928, the census directed by the present writer succeeded in obtaining a complete count of the bird population of 8·3 square miles, and there seems to be no record of this comparatively minute field ever having been surpassed in any comparable survey. Nor, looking back on the labour and fatigue involved, is this particularly surprising. While it would undoubtedly be feasible in an open plain with little cover or obstruction and a low bird population to make a complete census of a considerably larger tract there are many types of ground where even eight square miles would be far too much to undertake. In fact, for heavily wooded mixed country with a high density of bird life 40 acres, or one-sixteenth of a square mile, is quite as much as a single observer can comfortably cover. And there is no worse illusion in census work than to suppose that if one man can cover 40 acres, two can cover 80, and ten 400 and so forth. A more probable ratio in practice is 50 to 60 acres for two observers and perhaps 150 at the outside for ten of them. The reasons for this disappointing increment must be clear to anyone who has taken part in much work of this kind in the field. In the first place each successive observer is likely to be less competent than the last, and there are few places on earth where anything like ten men can be raised without including some who are bound either to imperil the standard of accuracy or to hold the rest back. Then the difficulties of co-ordination rise steeply with each extra observer, and since overlapping must be avoided census work tends to be reduced to the pace of the slowest member or the one with the most difficult task at any given moment. When it is borne in mind that a simultaneous turnout for several hours' field work of a number of usually busy persons at frequent intervals presents further problems to the organiser the reasons for suggesting that a complete individual bird census is really a one-man or two-man job will perhaps be apparent. Help, of course, is valuable, but a surprising amount can be got through without it.

Preliminary Survey

The first business in carrying out a complete census is to survey and get a thorough knowledge of your area. A map is the basis of every census, and it will normally be necessary to obtain or sketch for yourself an outline map on a scale of

OXFORD BIRD CENSUS.				
Name E. M. Nicholson : Date 25.10.27				
BIRD	A	B	C	D
BLACKBIRD	1,1,	—	1,2,4,3,	1,1,1
CHAFFINCH	—	2,6,1	2,1,3	—
ROBIN	1,	4,4	1,	4,4
STARLING	—	25,73	—	—
Mistle thrush	—	—	1	—
Blue tit	—	3,1,	—	1
Great tit	—	2,	—	—
Partridge	—	—	14	—
Moorhen	—	—	—	1
Kestrel	—	1	—	—

Fig 4. This card is filled up to illustrate method used in operations. The first area, a small field, goes in Col. A and other fields in Cols. B.C. & D. Names of four common species are printed on the card for convenience, others being written below as required. The numbers noted in each division are put down as they occur: at the end of the day all observers' cards are collected and totals entered in the permanent record with an account of weather conditions and so forth.

at least six inches to the mile. In England and Wales this scale is obtainable from the Ordnance Survey, and also a 25-inch scale which is desirable for gardens, coppices and other congested areas. In almost every case the landowner possesses a suitable map which can be borrowed and traced. Since the usefulness of census work largely depends on how closely it can be linked up to a definite extent of country it is important to choose boundaries which either enclose a known acreage, or else are so geometrical that the acreage can be precisely worked out. That the Anglo-Saxon world should work in acres, and the Continental in hectares is regrettable, but in present circumstances there seems no help for it except a good conversion table. The field of operations may be selected on a variety of principles. It may be intended to be as fair as possible a sample of a more or less considerable tract of surrounding land. It may represent one of the richest concentrations of bird population apparent in the district, or one of the sparsest. It may be typical of some peculiar habitat, such as virgin woodland, or a farm under grass, or an island or a small town. It may be selected from an ecological standpoint as ground which is undergoing or about to undergo some wholesale change—the site of a building estate or

G

afforestation scheme, a marsh about to be drained, waste land due for cultivation or the bed of a future reservoir. In this case the census will derive its value from being repeated at intervals during the process of change, and in fact every census gains much from repetition, which emphasises fluctuations and trends of population not otherwise discernible. Of course, some areas make much more interesting and significant census fields than others, but there is still none which cannot yield something of importance if tackled with persistence and skill. The essential thing is that the reasons for selecting the field of operations and its topographical characteristics should be fully analysed in recording the results.

Dividing up the Field

Having chosen and mapped the field of operations the next task is to divide it into sections. This part of the work is much more important than it may at first glance appear. There are sound alternative principles on which it may be based. The first is to employ a mathematical grid system of equal squares of convenient extent—say, 1 to 4 acres. The advantage of this method is that the sections are all equal and are probably free of any subjective bias. The drawback is that they take no account of topographical divisions and are difficult to trace accurately on the ground. The alternative is to use natural sections of convenient size—fields, copses, gardens and so forth. The larger ones may profitably be subdivided along the lines of roads, paths, woodland rides, fences, hedges, and streams, or along imaginary lines between prominent landmarks. It is important to remember that a hedge or stream itself should never be used as a boundary in bird-census work— any boundary based on it should be taken as running parallel at an interval of say ten yards on one side or the other. The reason for this is that hedgerows and watercourses are not divisions, but thoroughfares and dwellings for birds, and that a failure to recognise the fact must lead to endless practical difficulties.

Executing the Census

Assume now that you have chosen the field of operations, made or secured a large-scale outline map of it and divided it into suitable working sections. In the process you will have acquired already a rather close knowledge of the bird population. Outside the breeding season an adequate census may probably be taken in one day, provided the area is not too large. It will be worth leaving the fair-copy outline map at home and using rough sectional sheets for scribbling down results in the field. The field must be worked section by section in the order that common sense dictates ; thus if there is found to be in the preliminary survey any substantial daily movement between the various sections you must avoid counting one section affected before the exodus takes place from it and another after birds already counted have poured into it, or on the other hand missing the birds concerned at both points. It must be understood that chance movements, apart from local disturbance or regular foraging, roosting or migratory journeys, are not a serious factor ; the bird-watcher who really knows his ground and its birds need rarely be troubled by them. Fields containing large species like Rooks, Jackdaws, Lapwings and so forth should be counted from suitable cover before entering them, and again when the birds are flushed, which should be done in such a direction as to drive them, if possible, to a point outside the field of operations. Open country should be counted in a block and more or less continuous woodland in the same way, instead of sections of each alternately, since movement is much more likely to occur within such units than between them.

That is to say, it is wiser to work all one type of habitat first and then all of a second and a third in succession rather than to proceed in a series of arbitrary cross-sections which involve doing a bit of wood and a bit of open and then perhaps a bit of swamp and then the same again in a different order.

Margin of Error

Theoretically it is easily possible for such small inconspicuous creatures as many birds to evade the census; in practice the risk is not serious. A skilled bird-watcher, with a good ear for common call-notes and a reasonably sharp eye, quartering the ground on beats close enough to exclude the likelihood of birds in the intervening space being missed through anything short of close skulking, will be fairly sure, provided he is not hurried, to arrive at a figure showing less than 15 per cent. margin of error, and with favourable conditions less than 5 per cent. either way. Precise accuracy may sometimes be obtainable, but is not necessarily worth attaining. It must be understood that for any ordinary area bird population is not a fixed quantity, but something fluctuating slightly from day to day or from hour to hour, through wanderings, casualties and other factors. If it were possible to take by some uninvented mechanism a sort of snapshot bird census of photographic accuracy, say, four times a day for a month, the results would by no means all tally, and anyone working them up would be reduced to concluding that the mean, or possibly the mode,[1] of the various totals was the only single figure which could stand plausibly as representing the bird population in question. On either side of that figure would be a margin representing birds which had vanished or died, or newly appeared during the month, together with a number living partly across the boundary which might or might not be present within the defined limits at the moment when the census was taken. The extent of this margin, of course, would vary with the locality. In the case of roosting sites and so forth it might be of the order of hundreds per cent., and it would rarely be less than say 10 per cent. Generally speaking, the larger the area the smaller this margin of fluctuation tends to be, since clearly the proportion of pairs overlapping the boundary of a ten-acre plot must be far higher than the proportion for a thousand-acre plot, and so on. It is important to understand this fact, for on it depends the claim that a competently conducted bird census gives prac-

---

[1] *i.e.*, the figure most frequently occurring, as distinct from the average between extremes and intermediate figures.

tically as fair a view of the total bird population of most areas as it is theoretically possible to secure.

Of course if the count can be checked, either on the same day or later, it is always worth doing, and in any case difficult bits, such as gardens, woodland, and so forth should be re-counted wherever possible, the highest reliable figure being adopted. Where several bird-watchers take part, constant care is necessary to avoid interference either by flushing birds ahead on one another's beats, or by double counting or otherwise. In case of doubt whether a bird or birds may have been counted by more than one man the point should be discussed and settled on the spot as soon as the beat is finished, while the details are still clear in the mind. It should be a general rule not to count birds which fly over without alighting unless they are definitely foraging above the area, like Swallows, Kestrels and so forth. Exception might also defensibly be made in favour of birds which almost undoubtedly would have alighted but for the presence of the observer —this applies especially to such species as Duck.

A Census in the Breeding Season

The taking of a complete census in the breeding season raises quite distinct problems. Here a

count taken on a single day is probably valueless,
even for quite small areas. The census should be
spread over the entire season, or as much of it as
possible. At an early stage after a survey of the
ground a tour should be made of it and all singing
cocks marked on the sketch-map. Where a mate
is present the figure 2 may be added to denote a
pair, and as soon as evidence of a nest is available
it may be indicated by a cross. It is unnecessary
to find the nest; adults carrying material repeatedly or food, the chittering of young waiting
for food in holes or inaccessible nests, or any
equally strong clues may safely be accepted. Of
course wherever a nest can be found and the
number of young reared ascertained the results
will be the richer for it. Thus we have four categories :

Chaffinch s. represents a singing male.
Chaffinch 2   ,,   a pair.
Chaffinch 2x   ,,   a pair definitely nesting.
Chaffinch 2x+4 ,,   a pair rearing 4 young.

Subsequent broods can be added separately
after a further plus sign. In some cases further
categories may be necessary for unmated hens or
immature birds, or non-breeding parties, but in
most areas suitable in scale for a complete individual census these occur only as transients.

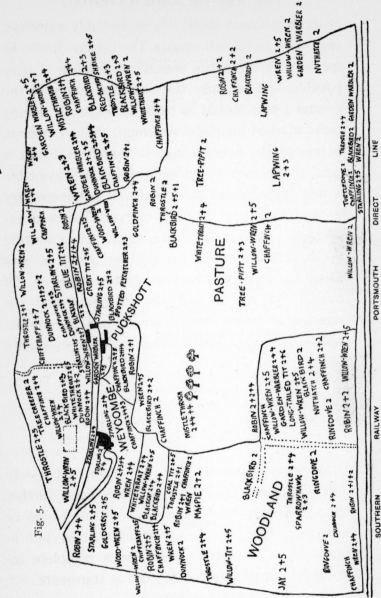

Fig. 5.

The method here recommended is illustrated by the map (Fig. 5). It contrasts with the method used by C. J. and H. G. Alexander in their pioneer census work near Tunbridge Wells during 1908, and also with that of the United States Bird Census, both of which were based on a simple count of singing males. The unreliability of this procedure has been so strongly brought out by recent work on the territory question that its abandonment can hardly be postponed. Far from representing the strength of breeding pairs the number of singing males proves to consist largely of unmated birds, and partly also of those which have lost first broods. While much remains to be learnt it is clear that in several species at least song either ceases or falls off so heavily after the nest is complete, or after hatching that the error resulting from this assumption is liable to be severe. Moreover, any method which gives a breeding season population in terms of pairs only must ignore the often considerable number of unmated birds, and its value in consequence starts at a discount. Wandering silent hens, or nomadic bands of immatures may have to remain outside the scope of a small-scale individual census, but there can be no excuse for not facing the major problem of the sedentary unmated male. For a choice of evils Schiermann's practice of confining his survey to proved breeding pairs is no doubt preferable to the U.S. Bird Census practice of assuming that a singing male represents a pair.

Summary of Individual Method

To sum up, the complete census of individuals is an operation normally confined by its exacting nature to a small area, with a maximum ranging perhaps from 40 acres to about 10 square miles according to the type of country. Its indispensable basis is a map by which the bird population can be related to the extent of ground inhabited. In order to bring out inequalities and changes of density the field of operations should be subdivided either on a grid basis or by sections suggested by the topography. Sections should not cut across different types of habitat ; a meadow, a garden or farmyard and a wood should form separate sections, both for convenience in counting and to avoid obscuring features special to the bird population of each of them.

Outside the breeding season such a census may be undertaken, after adequate preliminary work, in one day, but results should be checked at least in the more difficult sections. Numbers for different sections should on no account be lumped together or confused, either in the field or in subsequent reports.

During the breeding season the census must be built up by repeated rounds at not more than

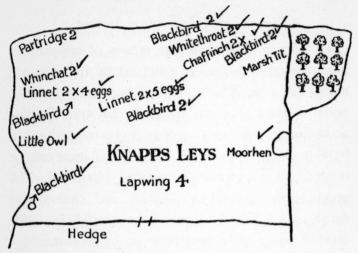

Fig. 6. Fragment of an actual field sketch-map for a Summer Bird Census, some of the names ticked to show which birds were again met with on a later check.

weekly intervals, marking on sketch-maps the singing males, pairs, and nesting pairs by separate symbols or script, and checking them on each occasion until the final number of breeding and non-breeding adults, and if possible of young reared has been arrived at. A singing male should not be accepted as evidence either of a pair or of a nest.

(b) SECTIONAL CENSUS

The complete individual census, as we have seen, is the most perfect census technique of its kind so far developed, although no doubt many improvements remain to be made in it. Its great drawback, however, is precisely this wealth of detail which confines its scope to relatively minute areas. Often it must be desirable to secure information about the bird population of much larger tracts of country. In this case the complete individual census must give way to more rough-and-ready methods which can be used rapidly, on a large scale, and with a reasonable although obviously reduced degree of accuracy. The best-known of these alternatives is the sectional census.

Use of Vehicles

The sectional census may be conducted from almost any sort of vehicle. It has been used fairly successfully on foot, on journeys by road and railway, and on ocean liners. It is highly adaptable, and can be applied either to a steep altitudinal survey on a mountain climb or to a voyage of thousands of miles. Its supreme drawback is that it cannot accurately be related to a definite extent of land or water ; its field is simply the field of view, or an arbitrary part of it, on one or both sides of the route. This field expands and contracts from time to time according to visibility or to such external interferences as tunnels, cliffs, gorges, forests, coasts or river banks. A further disadvantage is the subjective nature of a count where quickness of identification is often demanded and there can usually be no going back to have another look, and where there is undoubted scope for a difference of results corresponding rather to a difference of ability in the observers than to a difference in bird population.

In spite of these shortcomings the sectional census must be rated fairly high. While it is true that the precise extent of land or water covered must remain unknown it can be estimated with a useful degree of accuracy, since the distance covered whether by road, rail or water can always be ascertained and fluctuations arising from the varying size of the field become relatively insignificant owing to the great distances spanned by this method.

Comparability and Bias

The subjective handicap may be serious in comparing the results of different bird-watchers—this lack of comparability certainly tells against the sectional census—but at any rate the results of any given observer in various fields are safely comparable, and it should not be impossible eventually to work out what allowance should be made in comparing the results of different observers. It must be borne in mind that the sectional census can readily be linked up with the individual census by the simple process of conducting it across the same field and comparing results. A sectional census obviously exaggerates the numbers of conspicuous species and minimises the strength of retiring ones ; it cannot, except where no cover exists, be accepted as giving an unbiased picture. How strong the bias is depends on circumstances. Taken on foot, with plenty of time it may hardly yield in comprehensiveness to a complete individual census, while taken from a fast train it may make no pretence at recording anything of lower calibre than Rooks, Wood-pigeons and birds of prey.

Function of Sectional Census—Alpine Census

The function of a sectional census on foot is properly to link up a succession of different types of habitat. If all the country covered is of more or less the same type it will obviously be more appropriate to take a complete individual census or a series of samples. Probably the ideal task for a sectional census of this kind is for exposing a biological gradient ; that is to say, cutting a cross-section across a wide range of contours from a valley avifauna at the lower levels towards a mountain avifauna at the top. I have done this in the Alps of Dauphiné from the flat valley of the Romanche (2370 feet) to an elevation of 10,300 feet on the flanks of the Meije. The sharp zonation at various levels was in excess of expectation, and while the estimated density fell to 0·4 birds per 100 acres in the barren Alpine Chough zone above 7240 feet it was highest, not on the valley floor, but about the top of the tree-zone between 5300 to 5700 feet, where it reached approximately 7·8 birds per acre. Lower down it varied between 2 to 4 per acre. The basis of these figures was arrived at by calculating distances from the official survey (État-Majeur) and checking the breadth of field at intervals by pacing. Although the work was carefully done they obviously cannot claim the accuracy of densities worked out on a known acreage. The contours being taken from the map are nearly exact, and it is in showing the remarkably narrow limits of altitude within which such species as the

H   113

Whinchat, Tree-pipit and Skylark appear, become common and again fall out of the picture that the chief value of the operation consists. In Great Britain the range of altitudes is too small and their effect too insignificant to bring such spectacular zonation, but a cross-section divided up according to contours might still be worth undertaking in mountain districts. If such hindrances as steep-sided valleys are included it is best to observe a limit of say 100 yards on either side throughout, in order to eliminate the adventitious interference of an expanding and contracting field of view.

A sectional census on foot might also be used with advantage for exposing the gradient of bird-life outwards from the centre of a great town through suburban to rural areas, or from an estuary over marshes to cultivated uplands. In order to be of value, and to discount its inherent larger margin of error it ought to cover a fair distance—probably not less than five miles.

Counting from Train

The sectional bird census made on road or railway journeys is inevitably much more sketchy, but nevertheless may have a certain value of its own. The private car, unless open and running

through open country, is an unsuitable vehicle
for this work, and the motor coach is reported
also to be unsatisfactory, but from a not too
crowded train running at not more than 40 to
50 miles an hour bird-counting can be not only a
convenient means of passing the time but an
agency for throwing light on certain aspects of
bird population. Clearly many if not most species
will be left out of such a count, while the varying
speed of the train and the varying openness of
the country will considerably affect the figures.
Yet for the large conspicuous species with which
it deals the train count can give a significant and
roughly comparable index for different seasons.
I have used it in various countries, from Ireland
to Germany, Italy, France and South America,
while it has also been employed in Australia, West
Africa and elsewhere. The track being arbi-
trarily fixed (although with a strong bias towards
valleys and urban areas), and the length of any
section along which a count is taken being easily
ascertainable the train count possesses at least
some of the elements of comparability ; provided
that the limits and side observed are noted, together with the hour and date, the approximate
speed, weather, and anything else likely to affect
the figures, a sufficient frame can be provided to

exhibit quite plainly all the cruder fluctuations in different countries and at different seasons. The close correspondence between successive counts in similar conditions is an indication that the method is not nearly so unreliable as it may look at first glance. The gradation over large areas is better shown than by any other means at present available ; thus in crossing Ireland from Dublin to Connemara the average number of birds per mile on the eastern section, to Mullingar, was about 26, on the middle western, from Athlone on, it was just over 14, and on the extreme western in Connemara it fell to 3. In Italy, on the stretch from Turin up to the Mont Cenis frontier at Bardonecchia, the route fell into three general sections, Plain, Hill and Mountain, and the bird population (18th July 1927) changed like this :

(Numbers represent percentages of total in each case.)

Bird	Plain	Hill	Mountain
Swallow	24	12	0
Swift	0	9	80
Italian Sparrow	50	65	6
Small birds : Species (?)	20	8	1·4
All others	6	6	12·6
	100	100	100

Such a table shows that in spite of the large number of birds which must escape identification

topographical and seasonal changes over large
areas are remarkably clearly indicated.

Transect at Sea

Probably the greatest field for the sectional
census is at sea. Here, where other census methods
are incapable of application, and where the relatively slow-moving steady ship with its uniform
and never excessive speed offers an ideal platform,
the sectional method finds its element. The fact
that most liners carry considerable numbers of
people with nothing better to do than to look out
for birds puts the observer in an exceptionally
strong position. The wide unobstructed field of
vision and the ease with which distances can be
checked from the ship's log and positions recorded
are further advantages. It is true that in rough
weather the bird-watcher may find other pre-
occupations, or at least become inclined to dispute
whether the ship can even be described as a
relatively steady vehicle, but on balance the
oceanic transect has much to recommend it. If
it were taken up at all frequently on some of the
regular shipping routes, and on special cruises,
where few persons on board are ever so usefully
occupied, it would be possible within ten years to
gain a remarkably precise knowledge of the

seasonal distribution of pelagic birds. It is not even fantastic to imagine that by such means the prospects of a complete knowledge of distribution at sea are brighter than the immediate prospects of it on land, where large tracts of the African, South American, Arctic, Australian and Asiatic hinterlands must remain for many decades very inadequately worked.

The most convenient basis for an oceanic transect is the sample ten-mile count. The procedure is to read the ship's log, or have it read if it is inaccessible to passengers, if possible about the same time each day, and to count every bird seen during the following ten miles' run. Close to land or fishing banks, or in other special circumstances, two or three such counts daily may be advisable, while in such vast birdless areas as the Sargasso Sea a ten-mile count would yield almost consistently *nil*, and a note of any birds observed at all during the day must take its place. In any case observation should not be confined to the ten-mile count, which serves simply to obtain a value for the bird population comparable with other parts of the ocean ; a general impression of the number of species and their relative abundance, together with any special notes and the weather and latitude and longitude should be put down every day.

Such a detailed transect shows precisely how with increasing distance from land or the transition from one region to another the character of the bird life alters ; like so many sectional census undertakings it brings out a sharpness of divisions rarely appreciated by the casual bird-watcher who is content to rely on his own impressions. Six transects of this type have lately been made across the North Atlantic ; two by the present writer on the Hebrides-Greenland route in June and August 1928 (*British Birds*, XXII, 122-133), three on the London-West Indies route by E. M. and B. D. Nicholson in July, October and December 1929 (*British Birds*, XXIV, 266-274), and one by V. C. Wynne-Edwards on the Southampton-Quebec route in September 1930 (*Discovery*, XI, 359-362). The last of these is illustrated by the map (Fig. 7). Wynne-Edwards' suggestion that the inshore, offshore and oceanic zones may be equated with a Gull zone, an Auk zone and a Petrel zone deserves attention.

(c) CENSUS BY SAMPLE

The special function of census by sample is less clearly demarcated than those of other methods, because it has so far been less used. It represents an attempt to combine the precision and completeness of the individual method (*a*) with the wider scope of the cross-section (*b*). Where great tracts of country show no appreciable variety of fauna, as in deserts, on steppes, prairies or pack-ice, the sample is obviously the most suitable census method. It checks its own assumption ; if the whole region sampled really shows no appreciable differences in the density or composition of its bird population then the sample results ought to correspond very closely with one another. Here a section would only establish the same thing with perhaps more labour and certainly less precision. When the sample is used for areas admittedly showing great contrasts between one part and another its fitness becomes more questionable. In order to give valid results in this case it must be backed by a very exhaustive knowledge of the terrain, which will enable the bird-watcher to state with assurance what proportion of it belongs to the same type as one sample, and what to another. It involves, in fact, a prolonged preliminary survey to establish how many distinguishable types of habitat are included, how uniform their bird populations are, and how samples may be arranged so as best to cover them. It becomes accordingly the least fool-proof of all

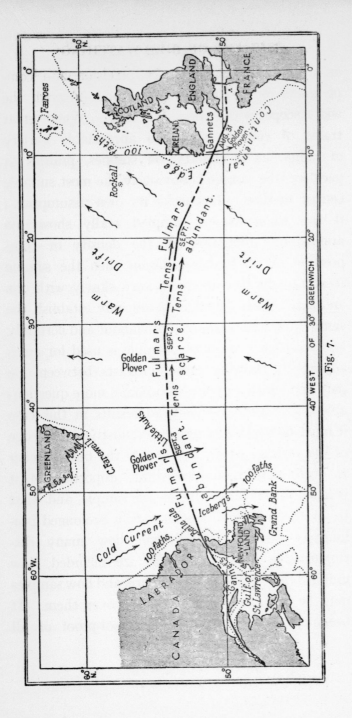

Fig. 7.

census methods : in fact it can hardly be undertaken successfully unless its result is fairly accurately known in advance.

Schiermann's Sample

Probably the best example of this method is
Gottfried Schiermann's sample census of the Unterspreewald near Berlin.[1] After preliminary work
since 1923 he surveyed the bird population of this
forest area of some 10·8 square miles with the aid
of a series of 16 control plots each 250 metres
square during 1928-9, obtaining a population of
2729 breeding pairs belonging to 97 species. Operations were evidently conducted with great thoroughness, but such accuracy as the figures possess
appears due rather to the excellence of the preliminary study than to the efficiency of the sample
method. In the last resort the totals depend less
on the statistical data of the sample plots than on
the observer's personal estimates of the extent of
ground to which each is properly applicable. As
indicating the subjective and misleading nature
of the approach it is particularly worth noting the
writer's conclusion in favour of superseding such
terms as " common " and " rare " by " low,

[1] Gottfried Schiermann, " Studien über Siedelungsdichte im
Brutgebiet," *Journal für Ornithologie*, LXXVIII., 1930, 137-180.

medium, or high density." "High density" implies a species living in the centre of its range and exploiting the most favourable ecological conditions to the full. Among examples from the Unterspreewald he gives the Chaffinch, with a density of about one pair per 26 acres as "high density." But at Weycombe, Surrey, in 1926 I found an average of 7 adult Chaffinches per 8 acres in the breeding season, while B. D. Nicholson found 2·3 adult chaffinches per acre on 20 acres in Ayrshire throughout May, so that by British standards Schiermann's "high density" would rank as "medium" if not "low."

This gives yet another proof of the danger of depending on any measure for bird population except definite figures for known areas reliably ascertained. Despite these unwarranted deductions Schiermann's paper stands as easily the best model of a sample census successfully put in practice under difficult natural conditions, and there seems no reason whatever to suspect its accuracy so far as it goes. In a sense any complete individual census may count as a sample for a larger area : the evident distinction is that whatever wider conclusions may be drawn from it the complete individual census stands on its own merits in any case, while a sample census bases itself on plots too small to have any separate validity apart from the larger survey which they support.

(d) SPECIFIC CENSUS

The specific census is the oldest and most developed form of bird census, and in some ways the most remunerative. By selecting a suitable species and concentrating on it a great deal of ground can be covered where modern transport facilities exist. Cars, in fact, have enabled the specific census to be organised on a national scale with a remarkably high degree of accuracy, and this method, which was first fully exploited by the *British Birds* Census of Heronries in 1928, seems certain to be increasingly used. The census of Common Buzzards in Devon by the Devon Bird-watching Society, and the census of rookeries undertaken in the Oxford district by the Oxford Bird Census, in Derbyshire, Nottinghamshire and thereabouts by Roebuck, and in other parts of England, Scotland and Wales, are further examples of the progress in this branch, while the Great Crested Grebe Enquiry, 1931, makes the second organised specific census of national scope.

Choice of Subject

While any species might be chosen as the subject of statistical inquiry by a resolute and able bird-watcher, there are clearly some which are much more suitable to the method than others. The qualities which determine this are chiefly conspicuousness and predictability. Under the first head Herons, birds of prey, Crows, Pigeons, Lapwings, Curlews, Swallows, House-martins, Cormorants, Gannets, and a number of other species fall appropriately. The second includes species which without necessarily being conspicuous themselves are limited to particular habitats where they can readily be traced, expecially in the breeding season, such as Grebes, Coot and Duck on inland waters, Sand-martins at sandpits and embankments, Wheatears on open wastes, Ringed Plovers on shingly or sandy coasts, Ring-ousels on high moorland and so forth. To choose some such species and to carry out an intensive investigation of it over some such area as a county or a considerable part of one is among the most promising tasks that any bird-watcher can at present take up. It has the extra advantage of facilitating a special study of the life-history of the species, or of such aspects as reproduction, food, movements, or relations with competitors.

Map Foundation

The specific census, like all others, must be based on the map, and it is highly important that whatever size or shape of area is tackled the count should be complete within definite noted limits. It is useless to attempt a county or a district if patches within the field of operations are not fully covered. Nor can the boundaries be too carefully chosen. A county, despite or because of the fact that it is zoologically a preposterous unit, often makes a good arbitrary field, and has the great advantage of precise boundaries which are easily traced not only by the census-taker but by anyone else. A so many mile radius round a given point is not to be recommended; its limits and extent are too difficult to follow. A good alternative is to use the 1-inch ordnance map (3rd Revision) with its regular squares on a 2-mile base. The great advantage of this is that density of population in any part can readily and precisely be compared with density in any other.

The specific census, unlike other types, loses rather heavily by being attempted outside the breeding season. It relies for success on a fairly full preliminary survey to locate either the actual nest-trees, nest-holes or breeding waters of the bird in question, or at any rate all those on which it may possibly occur, so that when the season comes there is no more question of scouring the country-side, but only of going the rounds of actual or potential haunts and making a count, which should if possible be checked before the end of the season, at any rate once. While the breeding pair is the natural unit of a specific census every effort should be made to secure counts or estimates of non-breeding stock.

Recording Census Results

Perhaps the hardest part of bird census work comes after the field operations are over, with the task of working up data for publication or filing. Not to leave out anything essential to under-standing either of the full material or of the methods on which it is based is difficult enough : to do it without running to such length that the most obliging editor must rebel is apt to prove the last straw. The mere totals of species and in-dividuals with the area on which they were found are an insignificant fraction of a good bird census paper. It is necessary to make clear the nature of the ground, its ecology and climate and liability to disturbance, the boundaries by which it may

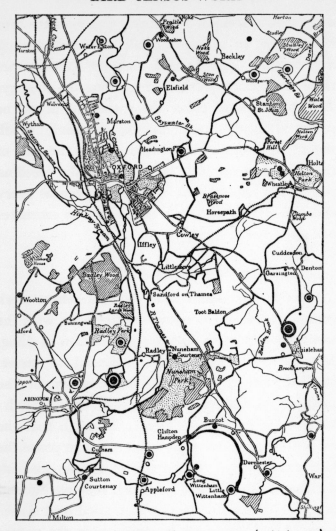

Fig 8 • Isolated nests (total below 5). ○ Very small rookeries (total below 25).
● Small rookeries (total below 75). ◉ Medium rookeries (total below 200).
◉ Large rookeries (total above 200). Map showing distribution of
rookeries in the Oxford District, based on the Ordnance Survey Map.

be correctly identified, perhaps many years later, the dates and circumstances of the count, and the names of those who took part in it, any factors which suggest or prove a variation at any point from normal, any local historical details which bear on the matter, the total not only for the area as a whole but for the various sections of it, accounting if possible for sharp rises or falls above or below the general average, the incidental observations which were made, definitions of the terms used and of the evidence required as proof of a pair, a nest and so forth. The wealth of detail required in a census report demands a corresponding economy of words.

CHAPTER IV

CONTEMPORARY TASKS OF BIRD-WATCHING

Bird ecology—Classification of types of country in British Isles—
Investigating territory—Observation of nests—Bird-watching and
Bird-photography—Altitude and speed—Collecting—Bird-watching
on expeditions—Organised work—Line of advance.

BIRD ECOLOGY

BIRD ecology—the relation of birds to the rest of
the animal and plant world, and to one another—
is still an almost virgin field. For the bird-watcher
who is competent and determined to tackle it, it
offers possibilities which are not exceeded in any
other direction, but it is so far-reaching, demanding
such efforts and such a firm flexible grasp that to
enter it is undoubtedly an ambitious undertaking.
Elsewhere the bird-watcher may succeed with a
narrow concentrated outlook, or escape failure
despite a chronic dissipation of energies. Bird
ecology is more exacting : it demands concentration and breadth together, which are not an easy
combination to find.

Botanists have worked out pretty thoroughly

BIRD-WATCHING SIMPLIFIED—TAMENESS OF A GREENLAND PTARMIGAN.

Photograph by W. G. H. P. Crouch.

the peculiar communities of plants which are found in any special habitat, but bird-watchers have made very little effort to describe the corresponding communities of birds. A moment's thought will show that these communities are none the less real for being so steadily ignored. The southern English heath community with its dominant Willow-warblers, Chaffinches, Meadow-pipits, Linnets, Skylarks, Whitethroats, Stonechats, Cuckoos, Yellowhammers and so forth ; the sea cliff community, Guillemots, Razor-bills, Herring Gulls, Fulmars and Kittiwakes ; the arable land community of Skylarks, Lapwings, Buntings, Rooks, Jackdaws, and often Black-headed Gulls, are obvious examples which could be multiplied indefinitely. From another angle, it is abnormal to see a Bullfinch and a Wheatear together, or a Cormorant and a Partridge, or a Nightingale and a Little Tern, but normal to see a Bullfinch and a Nightingale, a Cormorant and a Little Tern or a Partridge and a Wheatear. The first pairs are taken from quite different communities, the second set from overlapping ones, and the incongruity of the former is adequate evidence that we recognise these bird communities sub-consciously and are shocked by their infringement, even if we never bother to work them out.

A published survey of bird communities, even of a single bird community, might be one of the most valuable contributions to the art of bird-watching that could be made at the present time. It might on the other hand be singularly futile and misleading, if undertaken without adequate study and adequate observation.

In order to investigate bird ecology one needs an awareness of the corresponding botanical methods and results without the barren and indefensible imitation which makes the line of least resistance. It is necessary at the outset to classify the types of habitat included, on a basis of avifauna as well as flora, which may involve lumping habitats separately distinguished by the botanists, or separating others which the botanists treat as one. The criterion must simply be whether the difference between one sort of habitat and another is sufficient to make any regular perceptible difference in the density or composition of the bird life.

It is discreditable that no fully worked-out agreed classification of this sort is available for the use of bird-watchers. Just as it has come to be understood in the United States and U.S.S.R., and begins even to be suspected in England, that one cannot deal with agricultural land as being simply so many acres of arable and so many of pasture, so it is forced on our notice in bird-watching that we can no longer defensibly talk of birds as belonging to woodland or moorland or grassland. We must be more explicit, if we are not to confuse ourselves and other people. In agriculture we must quote the acreage of land belonging to the various minutely classified types of soil, so that those interested can know at once, without needing to visit it, that so much of it is suitable for cereals, and so much for specific root crops, and so much for hay, while a certain extent may belong to a type unremunerative in present circumstances for any of these kinds of cultivation. These things used to be ascertained by trial and error spread over generations : a soil survey and a few sample analyses enable them to be read off at sight from a chart as accurately as the right grade of oil for the sump of a car or the right exposure for a photograph. Distribution of birds, which is still commonly described in terms of medieval literary nomenclature is equally capable, given some slight effort, of being reduced to precise order. The compilation of such a table, which can stand as a permanent basis of reference in bird-watching, comparable to the scientific genera and species which make the permanent basis of systematy, is evidently a job for an authoritative committee, employing material collected on a large scale by a suitable organisation. To hold strictly to this contention would be to argue that we must wait, at any rate some years more, for the basis of any accurate distributional work. In order to avert such delay I have already compiled and published (in *How Birds Live*, First Appendix) a Preliminary Classification of the Types of Country in Great Britain. Since such a classification is so urgently needed in bird-watching I make no apology for including it here in a revised form, although I am fully aware of the defects and inadequacies which must become manifest when the subject has been better explored.

CLASSIFICATION OF TYPES OF COUNTRY IN BRITISH ISLES

Coastal Group.

	Index No. A.B.C.
Rocky beach without cliffs. Type : Goring-by-Sea, Sussex	A 1
Rocky beach, with precipitous chalk cliffs. Type : Beachy Head, Sussex. . .	A 2
Rocky beach, with chalk undercliffs and rich vegetation. Type : Dowlands Landslip, Lyme Regis. . . .	A 3

Coustal Group—contd.

Rocky beach, with limestone cliffs. . .	A 4
Rocky beach, with Devonian cliffs. Type: Baggy Point, Devon	A 5
Rocky beach, with Devonian undercliffs and rich vegetation. Type: Combe Martin, N. Devon	A 6
Rocky beach, with basaltic cliffs and ledges	A 7
Shingly beach, with clay or sandstone cliffs. Types: Selsey, Sussex, and Hengistbury, Hants	B 1
Shingly beach without cliffs. Type: Pevensey Bay, Sussex	B 2
Muddy or sandy beach without cliffs . .	B 3
Muddy or sandy beach, with low terraced cliffs of clay	B 4
Sand dunes	C 1
Shingle tracts and foreshore. Type: Dungeness	C 2
Salt-water lagoons and brackish ponds. Type: Salthouse and Cley, Norfolk .	C 3
Deep arms of the sea	C 4
Shallow arms of the sea and tidal harbours	C 5
Salt marsh. Type: Wells-next-the-Sea, Norfolk	C 6

Inland Water Group

Index No.
D.E.

Estuarine, fresh and salt water alternately. Type : Fergus estuary, Co. Clare . .	D 1
Marshes and rushy fields. Type : Braunton Marsh, near Barnstaple . . .	D 2
River-levels, water-meadows and flood-land	D 3
Reed-beds	D 4
Broads, lowland meres and large ponds. Types : Hickling Broad . . .	D 5
Ponds and tarns on sand or peat. Type : Frensham, Surrey	D 6
Mountain tarns. Type : Near Windy Gap, Co. Kerry	D 7
Reservoirs for water supply : banks bare of vegetation. Type : Staines, Middlesex .	D 8
Deep lakes, mostly in mountainous parts. Type : Lough Derg	D 9
Ditto, but with bare uncultivated shores .	D 10
Lakes or ponds among woodlands . .	D 11
Small ponds with osiers in claypits, etc. .	D 12
Dykes and canals with standing water .	E 1
Rivers—broad, deep, lowland streams .	E 2
Rivers—fast mountain streams. Type : Rawthey, Sedbergh, Yorkshire . .	E 3
Brooks and small streams . . .	E 4

Woodland Group—contd.

Index No.
G.

Scots pine plantation, 25 to 50 feet tall .	G	3
Scots pine wood or forest fully grown .	G	4
Larch plantation, young, unthinned .	G	5
Larch plantation, fully grown . . .	G	6
Spruce plantation, young . . .	G	7
Spruce plantation, fully grown . . .	G	8
Low beech wood, with yew and holly. Type : Burnham Beeches . . .	G	9
Beech wood on the chalk, unmixed. Type : High Heavens Wood, near Marlow, Buckinghamshire	G	10
Hornbeam wood. Type : Epping Forest .	G	11
Close mixed coppice of low growth . .	G	12
Oak and ash : " Coppice with standards " .	G	13
Pure ash : calcareous association . .	G	14
Full-grown oak canopy	G	15
Hill-side oak scrub	G	16
Parks with lime, chestnut, etc., dominant .	G	17
Parks with oak dominant . . .	G	18
Parks with beech dominant . . .	G	19
Parks with elm dominant . . .	G	20
Woodland clearings	G	21

Cultivation Group.   H.

Meadows and hayfields above alluvial level	H	1

Cultivation Group—contd.
Index No.
H.

Permanent pasture and dales above alluvial level . . . . . . H 2

High hill pastures . . . . H 3

Arable laid down to grass. Type : near Elmstone Hardwicke, Gloucester . . H 4

Arable under corn (ploughed land or stubble) H 5

Ditto, Midland type with very large open fields. Type : Lincoln Ridge . . H 6

Arable under green crops (plough land) . H 7

Market gardens and allotments . . H 8

Flower and pleasure gardens . . . H 9

Private shrubberies (laurel-rhododendron association) . . . . . H 10

Churchyards, cemeteries, etc. . . . H 11

Public parks and ornamental gardens, urban . . . . . . H 12

Orchards, apple . . . . . H 13

Orchards, cherry . . . . . H 14

Orchards, other fruits . . . . H 15

Civilisation Group.
J.

Large buildings, churches, ruins, towers, etc. J 1

Farms, farmyards, etc. . . . . J 2

Hamlets and villages . . . . J 3

Market towns with a close core, but gardens round. Type: Marlow, Buckinghamshire J 4

Garden towns or loosely built suburbs.

    Type : Letchworth   .   .   .   .   J 5

Large towns interspersed with trees and

    gardens. Type : Cheltenham   .   .   J 6

Closed towns and slums. Type : Gloucester J 7

Large industrial towns with soot pall.

    Type : Leeds   .   .   .   .   .   J 8

Grassy stretches within towns. Type :

    Harrogate Stray   .   .   .   .   J 9

Railway cuttings, embankments, etc.   .   J 10

Roadsides and lanes with hedges   .   .   J 11

Roadsides and lanes with avenues of trees .   J 12

Roadsides and lanes with open sides   .   J 13

Narrow lanes with bushy banks   .   .   J 14

Chalk pits   .   .   .   .   .   .   J 15

Sand pits   .   .   .   .   .   .   J 16

Stone quarries   .   .   .   .   .   J 17

Collieries and mine pitheads   .   .   .   J 18

Docks and harbours   .   .   .   J 19

Such a classification as this will serve for current work, provided that elasticity is given it by modifying the rigid compartments where they are found inapplicable, subdividing them in cases where they are too wide or fusing two or three together where their bird populations appear to coincide. A finally valid classification must of course be very different. It must take account of climatic distinctions like that between the dry germanic eastern side of Britain and the damp oceanic western side : it must also be based on underlying differences of geology, drift and soil composition, or in the case of waters on their PH readings, their general biological gradation and so forth. Somehow it must tackle the translation from static into dynamic terms which this crude preliminary sketch cannot undertake. That is to say, the rigid labels must be reconciled with the fact that environments are continually changing, through natural causes or human interference, from one category to another in course of time, while in space also they shade off imperceptibly into one another almost as frequently as they occur sharply divided. What confronts us is the fact that an ideal basis for bird-watching classification of country depends on a skilful synthesis of ecological, climatic, geological, agricultural and many other data, a large part of which remains to be collected. Until such a synthesis is available it is less dangerous to carry on with a classification devised like this one, purely for bird-watching purposes, and capable of being moulded as research progresses, than to take over wholesale an equally inadequate one from botany or some other single part of the field.

The advantage of working with such a system is comparable to the advantage of mapping, or of taking a census. Once again the lazy, misleading, subjective methods have given place to a strict external control, forcing the bird-watcher to see things to which he has previously managed to remain blind. It is no longer possible, for instance, to describe the Nuthatch or the Bullfinch as woodland birds : the system demands exact scrutiny of which types of woodland they flourish in, which they inhabit more sparingly and which they are absent from altogether. One can no longer think loosely of the House-sparrow as being " an abundant and generally distributed species " : it emerges as a sharply restricted form confined to habitats in Group J and part of Group H.

A single bird-watcher working on these lines in one circumscribed district might considerably enlarge our knowledge of local distribution. He should, in adopting the classification here given, select his own types with which he is familiar ; some of the present writer's own type localities are quoted in the above list in order to suggest examples. A particularly important task is to discover for such common residents as the Rook,

K 145

Lapwing, Mistle-thrush, and so forth, which types of country are occupied in the breeding season, which in the following weeks, and which in winter. It is not yet realised how much local movement takes place between different types of habitat : field observation on these lines could tackle the question more effectively than ringing. Under each species must be noted the reference number of each habitat in which it is found, the density or frequency of its occurrence, and the dates. When completed such a survey must set a new standard of accuracy in the study of distribution. It would show at a glance at what points one species overlaps or competes with another, which species range over a wide variety of habitats and which are more narrowly distributed, which habitats are favoured in summer and which in winter, and so forth. Not only could all the habitats be read off for any given bird, but all the birds for any given habitat.

Comparison of results in different districts would no doubt show that the dominant species in a given habitat are not everywhere the same, and that some birds present, and perhaps dominant in one area, are absent from a similar community elsewhere, while others, perhaps, take their place. These discrepancies supply the clues which will take a first-rate bird-watcher far towards the solution of some of the chief living problems of bird life.

Under such an analysis the community ceases to be a rather vague conception of a handful of species living together, and becomes a pattern which can be dissected and compared, part by part, with other similar patterns, till the design becomes apparent.

INVESTIGATING TERRITORY

The investigation of territory represents probably the most fundamental advance that bird-watching has achieved this century. Here we are concerned less with the observations and their meaning than with the technique through which they have been reached. The development of this technique, and the elucidation of the subject, are primarily the work of a single man, Mr. H. Eliot Howard. His *Introduction to the Study of Bird Behaviour* is a work which the bird-watcher can scarcely afford not to read, and although it goes without saying that much remains to be done, no brief discussion such as we must be content with at this point can possibly do justice to the elaborate detail in which territory has been worked out.

THE ART OF BIRD-WATCHING

The secret of successful bird-watching in this, as in so many other fields, is an intense concentration of scope. Old field-naturalists used to apologise for confining their activities to one district or one parish : the solver of territorial problems should apologise if he finds it necessary to stray beyond the boundaries of one common, or one wood. To choose a sphere of operations so convenient and compact that it can usefully be visited at any spare hour, and that every inch of its surface can be intimately known is the essential condition for such work. It follows that a suburban open space or even a city park may make a wiser choice of ground than some distant bird-haunt which cannot be so frequently visited. The bird-watcher with a good stretch of common, marsh, meadow, woodland or beach at his door has, of course, a great advantage, so long as he can resist the greater distractions. In going over such a province for the first time one may see casually a Wren, a Robin, a Lapwing and so forth, just like that. But after a fortnight's acquaintance this casual atmosphere vanished : one recognises particular birds which are normally to be found at particular spots at a particular time of day. With this recognition the solution of mysteries has begun. The real bird-watcher is not a man who can say,

148

for example, " Look at that Tree-pipit ! " but the man who can ask, " What has happened to the Tree-pipit that belongs here ? " and having asked, can find it on its accustomed beat.

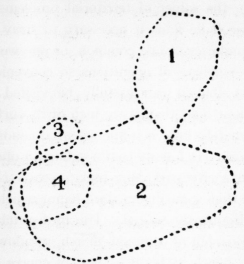

Fig 9. Example of Territory sketched in the field. Notice that while the territory of Nº1. is self-contained, Nº3's overlaps Nº2's while Nº4 (the last comer) actually carves out a large slice of Nº2's original claim.

A few acres of ground, not too crowded with birds, make the best starting-point for a study of territory. January or early February is the right season ; after May territory begins rapidly disintegrating. Only in case of selecting some wide-ranging single species, like an Owl or a Wood-pecker, should any wide field be attempted at first. Record from day to day any new arrival of a bird not previously present, any absence of a usual inhabitant, whether temporary or per-manent, and any change in the habits of the rest. These habits tend towards a steady routine, which can be recognised, as Eliot Howard's surveys show, much more easily than one might expect. By always having an outline sketch-map locating trees, hedges, pools or any other landmarks and by distinguishing the individual birds by num-bers, letters, names or symbols in order to enter their usual singing-stands, or roosts, or nest-sites, or feeding-places, the initial uncertainty which forbids individual bird-watching can rapidly be overcome. Once having got to know how many individuals there are, what territorial limits they observe, what routine they follow and what are their relations with one another, the field assumes a surprising clarity and richness of content. For the bird-watcher who is tied down to one spot, and able to undertake regular observation in the early mornings in spring territory offers one of the most promising subjects for field work : that it is so briefly treated here is due to the fact that

Eliot Howard's recent survey, which must certainly be read and digested by any observer in this field, has covered the ground so adequately as to render a more superficial account at best superfluous.

OBSERVATION OF NESTS

Casual reading of bird books gives the impression that an enormous amount of observation has been done at the nest, and it is hard for any except specialists to appreciate how serious the gaps still are. So much bird-watching of this kind has been vague, or scrappy, or unsatisfactorily recorded, that even among common species British records on obvious points may be inadequate or non-existent.

Jourdain, in a valuable recent paper,[1] supplies an authoritative and surprising list of the extent of these omissions. He shows that data concerning the incubation and fledging periods of British local races, and of such comparatively common species as Corn-bunting, Sand-martin, Chiffchaff and Wheatear remain to be published, while the many species for which supplementary observations are desirable include even the House-sparrow.

[1] "Our Present Knowledge of the Breeding Biology of Birds," by Rev. F. C. R. Jourdain, *British Birds*, XXIV., 138.

In order to prove useful such observations must be precise, and above all precisely recorded. Confusion has, in fact, arisen from an assumption that incubation begins with the laying of the last egg, when actually it may have begun earlier. In order to guard against such pitfalls Jourdain's paper should be referred to before beginning operations.

The share of each sex in building and incubation, although long ago recognised as a point for study, remains in many cases obscure. The time taken in building, construction of abortive or superfluous nests, and whether fresh material is added after laying or after hatching are questions worth attention.

When the young are hatched timing of the parents' journeys bringing food can be combined with specific observation to yield important results. As instances of extremes what I have myself recorded a pair of Greenland Wheatears (*Oenanthe oe. leucorhoa*) at Isersiutilik, South-west Greenland, provided their brood with forty-nine meals within an hour (*Ibis*, April 1930, p. 301), while a Guiana King Humming-bird (*Topaza pella*) with two young on the point of fledging brought food only ten times in more than seven hours' continuous watch (*Ibis*, July 1931, p. 544). In the first case feeding was direct, in the second by regurgitation.

BIRD-WATCHING AND BIRD-PHOTOGRAPHY

One of the more disappointing circumstances in contemporary ornithology is the waste resulting from the fact that many bird-photographers spend hours, or even days, on end in hides close to the nests of birds about which very little is known, without as a rule bothering to keep anything like a full and accurate record of what they see. A log-book showing times of visits of cock and hen, whether both usually come from the same or from different directions, what food they bring, how long they stay, which removes excrement and how often would always be of value. The rules which a bird-photographer might profitably follow are :—

(a) Always assume that every minute detail of the behaviour of birds under observation is unknown or unrecorded.

(b) Avoid limiting the interest to what strikes you as particularly interesting. What looks insignificant is very likely to prove of equal or greater value.

(c) Put down every precise note you can think of. For example, when a parent bird visits the nest, enter on every possible occasion the exact time, so that you can determine frequency ; the direction of approach, so that you can ascertain where food or material is brought from ; whether cock or hen, so that you can detect any differences, which are sure to exist, between their behaviour ; how long a stay is made, whether anxiety is shown, whether the visit is devoted entirely to the business in hand, or whether there is an idle pause ; what happens when both parents arrive simultaneously ; what happens when some intruder approaches ; whether alarm is excited by, for example, a passing bird of prey ; whether (when there are young in the nest) each chick is fed in turn, or haphazard ; when it begins to rain, or the wind rises, or sun comes out, and so forth.

In fact obedience to such principles is the secret of good bird-watching, where many of the major triumphs come from putting down observations and finding out as one goes along where they are leading. There is perhaps an apparent contradiction here of what has previously been said about the need for concentration and direction. The object must be to choose a strictly limited field, but within that field to follow without

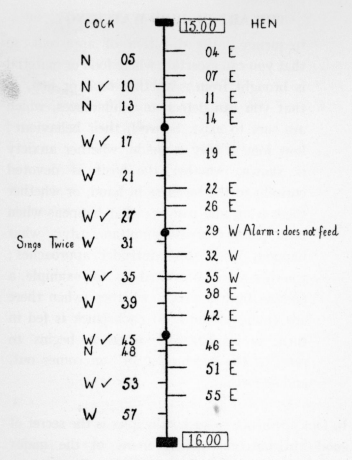

COCK			HEN
		15.00	
N	05	04	E
N ✓	10	07	E
N	13	11	E
		14	E
W ✓	17	19	E
W	21	22	E
		26	E
W ✓	27	29	W Alarm: does not feed
Sings Twice W	31	32	W
W ✓	35	35	W
W	39	38	E
		42	E
W ✓	45	46	E
N	48	51	E
W ✓	53	55	E
W	57		
		16.00	

Fig.10. In keeping intensive observation on a nest with young it is essential to avoid frequent distraction caused by entering up detailed notes, yet detailed notes must be kept. A solution is to employ some such system as that illustrated. The period of time- in this example between 3 and 4 p.m. represented by a perpendicular standard drawn in advance, and divided into 4 sections of a quarter-hour each. To avoid confusion of times the 24 hour clock is adopted. The left-hand side of the line is reserved for notes on the cock bird's activities, the right-hand for the hen's. Each visit is marked by a line showing the arrival time: e.g 07 in the right-hand column means that the hen arrives at 15.07, or 3.07 p.m. The direction of approach is indicated every time: it will be noticed, for instance, that till 3.26 the hen always comes up from the east, then three times from west, and afterwards from east again, while the cock usually forages in another direction. Occasions when excrement is removed from the nest are marked with a tick. Any other notes are readily entered in the margin, which should be wide. The great merit of such a system, compared with full verbal entries is that the exact time, and the bird concerned, cock or hen, are unmistakeably recorded, without having to be written out over and over again: writing is kept down to a minimum. The same principle can be applied for many other purposes: for instance in timing dives or duration of song, using one column for commencement and the second for end.

restraint wherever the clues take you. Bird-watching, then, involves in any given case a stage comparable to automatic writing, where you must transcribe nature without at first comprehending what you are transcribing. Only later, when the problems have emerged and defined themselves, can the bird-watcher take the initiative again by choosing what he means to pursue, and running it to a conclusion.

ALTITUDE AND SPEED

Precise information about the altitudes at which birds dwell or fly is still rather scarce. In Great Britain the altitude range is barely sufficient to yield any interesting zonation, but it is always worth being on the look-out for cases of lowland birds occurring, and especially breeding, above the 1000 feet contour or thereabouts, or conversely for low records of such high-ranging forms as Ptarmigan, Dotterel, Snow-bunting, or Ring-ousel in breeding quarters. Altitude of flight, although much harder to determine, is even more in need of study. As a rough visual guide it is worth remembering Lucanus' experiments, which showed that a Sparrowhawk was visible in outline at about 800 feet, and as a distinct speck at about 2100, disappearing from view towards 2800 ; for a Rook the three corresponding heights were about 1000, 2600 and 3000 feet ; a Buzzard remained visible in outline at about 2000 feet and a Lammergeier at about 3000. The accurate data so badly needed cannot be obtained from the ground without co-operation of several skilled observers using instruments of precision. A likelier method of obtaining them is by use of aircraft, which carry instruments giving a fairly reliable altitude reading at a glance, the difficulty here being that the noise of engine and airscrew, with heavier-than-air machines, or the noise and immense size of airships probably prejudice the chances of birds flying in their vicinity behaving in a normal way. The possibilities of a soaring glider or sailplane expertly used for following the movements of soaring birds have not yet been exploited. In spite of its limitations the glider has the great advantage of silence, and here evidently the pursuit of bird-watching as a sport and at the same time a science could find one of its most exciting outlets. In special circumstances on favoured migration routes a captive balloon might yield valuable data. It is important that in all records of altitude of flight full information should be included of weather, nature and altitude above sea level of ground, and whether

158

the birds observed were on migration, soaring, or apparently engaged in everyday flight.

Speed of flight has been ascertained for a fair number of species, but so many of the figures are based on one or two observed cases that repeated and systematic work is necessary in order to secure reliable averages as a basis for generalisations. This again is a job for at least two observers, who should use stop-watches, since the seconds hand of an ordinary watch is not accurate enough as a rule to avoid the risk of introducing a substantial error. Timing can only satisfactorily be done from the ground on a calm day : if there is any breeze direction and force must be noted, and checked at intervals. Stations must be chosen on a line over which a sufficient number of birds are likely to fly direct at a fairly uniform speed, such as a coast or river-bank, or a migration route, or a flyline between some regular roost or assembling-place and a foraging ground. There should be no bends, obstructions or differences of level, and the field should be free from disturbance. The observers must be able to signal instantly without misunderstanding. A base-line of half a mile in length is probably more suitable in most cases than a longer one where risk of error or frustration is increased.

Timing from cars or other vehicles can only give rough results, while aircraft, although able to supply airspeed readings, are liable to induce abnormal flight in birds near them.

COLLECTING

In some cases, especially overseas, the bird-watcher may find it necessary to collect specimens in order to identify the subjects of his observation, or to gain some essential information about them. It is highly unfortunate that the childish behaviour of a comparatively small number of men who have enjoyed amassing skins and eggs of birds from particular parts of the world, especially those of rare species, should have overlaid this subject with masses of unreason. The criteria which should be used are after all perfectly clear. No bird, no egg, no nest should be taken or destroyed merely because it is uncommon, or looks nice to collect, or may come in useful. In collecting the bird-watcher should limit himself strictly to whatever is needed to throw light on some particular problem which he wants to solve. It may be that a skin is required in order to establish the species, or race, or sex, or age, or that an egg must be destroyed in testing incubation. The task of the bird-watcher is to make up his mind whether collecting in a given case is essential to finding out what he wants to know, and if he decides it is he should carry out his decision ruthlessly and without sentiment. Where it is necessary to employ helpers, European or coloured, the collector is responsible for making sure that no impression is given them of collecting being either a profitable speculation to take up or desirable in itself.

Although collecting will usually be done with one specific object all possible resulting data should be recorded for the benefit of other workers. Thus where it is found necessary to collect specimens in order to confirm, for example, their sex or breeding condition, the skin should be preserved with a label stating the colour of bill, feet, iris, orbital ring and any other soft parts ; the crop and stomach should be examined for identifiable diet, and in appropriate cases the feet should be microscopically scrutinised for adhering seeds tending to throw light on movements or dispersal of plants, while a search for parasites, internal or external, may yield valuable information. Through a numbering system specimens should be linked wherever possible to field notes. It will not, unhappily, always be possible to carry out in full under stress of field work all that is obviously desirable, but undoubtedly much more convincing efforts in this direction could and should be made.

BIRD-WATCHING ON EXPEDITIONS

On scientific expeditions bird-watching naturally assumes a rather different character from normal home practice. For drawbacks, one is working among species whose habits and even identifications may be unfamiliar or unknown, and however long the expedition is to stay in the field time is always too short for anything approaching an ideal programme to be carried out. There are no museums or libraries to fall back on, apart from the few books it has been possible to bring out, and even the facilities for writing up notes and so forth may be far from comfortable. On the other hand, expeditionary bird-watching has peculiar assets. For the ornithological member or members there should, with luck, be no serious distraction from the work, beyond the physical demands of existence in uninhabited country. If the expedition is biological, in whole or in part, the presence of trained botanists, entomologists and zoologists in the same camp and working over the same ground gives opportunities for co-operative work, and for testing overlapping observations, which never come to the ordinary sedentary bird-watcher. The frequent interest of other members of the party in birds brings valuable help. Data on vegetation, climate, food and so forth, are forthcoming without waste of effort or delay. The chief dangers to be guarded against are the danger of not getting up the literature sufficiently well in advance, which leads to unnecessary hitches and uncertainty in the field, and the much more serious temptation to wander here and there collecting amusing fragments instead of selecting specific problems and investigating them in detail. Both these risks, of course, occur also at home, but they are more likely to prove fatal on an Expedition because of the shortness of time. For the same reason the technique to be applied, instruments to be used, and collaborators to be taken should be tested out some time in advance in order that inertia or friction through unfamiliarity should be overcome before they might jeopardise results. One ornithologist should certainly be taken on any biological expedition, and if much collecting is called for he should have an assistant taxidermist to leave him reasonably free for field work. In most situations there is ample work for two bird-watchers, and where conditions are really favourable three or more may be justified if the scale of the Expedition permits.

ORGANISED WORK

Possibilities of organised or co-operative bird-watching have scarcely begun to be exploited. Where several competent observers live in the same neighbourhood, and can agree on a definite programme the team may be able to achieve much more than the sum of individual effort. There is, of course, a danger, in assuming that numbers as such are necessarily a good thing. Neither the quality nor even the quantity of results increase in direct ratio to the number of observers employed, and it is unwise in field operations to believe too literally that many hands make light work : as everyone who has conducted large investigations is only too well aware, they may on the contrary make extraordinarily heavy work for the organiser, not all of which is remunerative. It is still hard, at this early stage, to distinguish which of the elements of friction occurring in practice are inherent in any attempt to use observers as a team and which are merely due to the general inexperience in such matters of organisers

A BIRD-WATCHING POST ON THE RIVER ESSEQUIBO. OXFORD UNIVERSITY BRITISH GUIANA EXPEDITION. 1929.

and observers alike. It would be misleading to dismiss the possibilities of controlling an army corps as extravagant on the strength of a few amateurish experiments with small squads of raw recruits. Looked at in such perspective the prospects for combined action, at any rate in Great Britain, are very satisfactory indeed. The first bird census on a national scale, the census of heronries in 1928, was actually carried through according to plan everywhere except in Scotland, and in spite of the utter inexperience of practically everyone taking part the standard of returns was on the whole highly creditable.

It may be doubted whether problems of large-scale organisation can be counted, strictly speaking, a part of the art of bird-watching. But since it seems certain that participation in such inquiries must become an increasingly frequent experience for bird-watchers a discussion of what they involve is not, in fact, irrelevant here. Any general investigation at once comes up against the difficulty that the lines on which bird-watching is organised are thoroughly out of date. You have the all-embracing British Ornithologists' Union in which bird-watchers remain a minority, with its organ, the *Ibis*, in which bird-watching problems are only occasionally discussed. You have the

Zoological Society and the Linnean Society, both of wide biological scope, whose respective *Proceedings* and *Transactions* sometimes include pure bird-watching papers. In a more contemporary direction you have the Ecological Society, with its *Journal of Ecology*, and its projected *Journal of Animal Numbers*, whose importance to the bird-watcher tends rapidly to increase. You have the Royal Society for the Protection of Birds, whose composition is sufficiently well known to require no comment, with its characteristic organ, *Bird Notes and News*. Regionally and locally you have natural history societies, scientific societies and field clubs, often with regular or intermittent publications of their own in which bird-watching problems receive varying prominence, much the most important being the Scottish Naturalists' Society. But in pure bird-watching you have no approach to a representative body ; that is to say, one which includes the majority of bird-watchers and no one who is not a bird-watcher. The gap is curious because there has been for more than twenty years a successful monthly, *British Birds*, run on this general basis. In fact the development of the ringing and trapping scheme and of census work has made the readers of *British Birds* the nearest approach to a working corporation of bird-watchers in this country. At the same time the need for specific societies of bird-watchers has been so strongly felt that at Oxford, at Cambridge, in Devon and elsewhere, organisations of this sort have appeared spontaneously since the War. Locally, these efforts have had useful results, but it is clear that the natural advance of bird-watching is now more and more handicapped by this chaotic diffusion of energies and results.

LINE OF ADVANCE

A Society of Bird-watchers on a national scale, and a central clearing-house for information and direction of team-work, present themselves with growing insistence as inevitable objectives. Released from the irrelevant cross-currents of a dozen or so outside interests and linked under a single inspiration bird-watching would undoubtedly be in a position to enter a period of intense creative effort. The things which such an organisation would have to provide in order to realise its opportunities are fairly clear. It would require the confidence and support of contemporary bird-watchers in general. It would need to build up a special library covering the entire literature relevant to bird-watching in this country. Such a library should find room for and index copies in typescript or manuscript of the great number of results of research which at present never find their way into print and remain scattered inaccessibly with their owners, often unknown to those working in the same field. It would need a directing committee for field studies which would be responsible for initiating and supervising all investigations on more than a local scale. With its regional affiliations and branches it would command the services of a powerful army of trained bird-watchers capable of being concentrated on specific problems simultaneously. It would accordingly be able to keep close touch with the Ministry of Agriculture, with other European ornithological centres and with related activities such as plant ecology, and to co-operate with them in its general scheme of work or in special inquiries. It might, for example, most usefully undertake a precise survey of the distribution of a set of typical species of restricted range, such as the Nightingale, Corn-bunting, Woodlark, Corncrake, Grey Wagtail, Redshank, Sand-martin, Redstart, Wood-warbler, Cirl-bunting, Red-backed Shrike, Nightjar, Stone-curlew, Ring-ousel, Tree-sparrow, Stock-dove, Turtle-dove, Great Crested Grebe, Coot, Tufted Duck, Common Sandpiper, Ringed Plover, Little Tern,

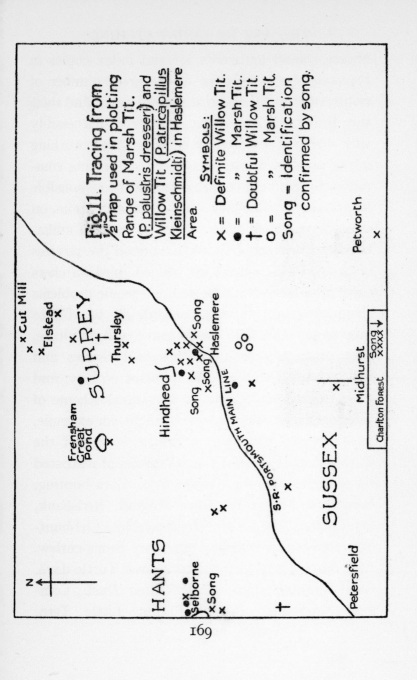

Fig. 11. Tracing from ½"=1 map used in plotting Range of Marsh Tit. (*P. palustris dresseri*) and Willow Tit (*P. atricapillus Kleinschmidti*) in Haslemere Area.

SYMBOLS:
× = Definite Willow Tit.
● = " Marsh Tit.
† = Doubtful Willow Tit.
○ = " Marsh Tit.
Song = Identification confirmed by song.

Lesser Redpoll, Twite, Black Grouse, Buzzard, Nuthatch, and various others characteristic of specialised habitats. Such a survey, linked up with an accurate ecological study in each case, would not only pave the way for a comprehensive scientific knowledge of bird distribution, but would be of immense value at this stage to those engaged in plant ecological surveys, soil surveys, and parallel lines of research all depending on similar climatic and biotic factors.

In order to undertake such tasks a Society of Bird-watchers would need some sort of bulletin to keep its members in touch, and some endowment to give the capital sums needed. It is conceivable that State grants from the Ministry of Agriculture or the Empire Marketing Board, such as are at present helping to maintain the Oxford Bird Census in its work on the Rook under the direction of Mr. W. B. Alexander, might be available for some of the research which should be undertaken, but such grants make too precarious and cramping a form of tenure to be satisfactory. They are, above all, too closely earmarked, for a Society of Bird-watchers would lose much of its value if it were not flexible enough to be in a position, say, to acquire at fairly short notice a nature reserve for experimental work, or to concentrate on matters like display whose economic significance is remote.

It must be recognised that in view of the traditions of bird-watching any such organisation would come to grief unless it could include without friction all sorts of varying temperaments and bents. It would have to reconcile within itself observers forming local teams working on their own lines, members of national investigations, independent research workers, some in museums and laboratories, some without scientific training and in remote places. To attain this flexibility without sacrificing impetus would be difficult, but it could be done, and unless it soon is done bird-watching will find itself from year to year more seriously starved even than it has been already. The new problems demand a new solution.

CHAPTER V

THE FIELD FOR BIRD-WATCHING

Limiting factors—Avoiding waste of time—Choosing ripe subjects—Life and mind of the individual—Conception of the pattern—Interpreting bird behaviour—Courtship problems—The locality decides the work.

INEVITABLY, in discussing how bird-watching is done, a good deal of discussion on the field for it has been anticipated. In order to avoid repetition, this chapter must take for granted such information on its subject as has thus incidentally been given already. That we should study the field for bird-watching from contrasting angles is by no means undesirable: in fact it may be said that if most bird-watchers had arrived in this way at anything like a clear idea of the field they have to work in, bird-watching would be at a much more advanced stage than it now is. Bird-watchers, like other inquiring men, naturally fail to solve their problem so long as they fail to state it.

LIMITING FACTORS

The potential field for bird-watching includes, of course, everything connected with the living bird.

The practical field, at any given time, is considerably more restricted. Among the limiting factors, three are obviously of supreme importance. First, it is futile devoting time to solve again those questions which have been solved already. Second, it is unprofitable to select problems so isolated from everything that has yet been done that their solution must be rendered impossible by want of relevant data on all sides. Third, the bird-watcher can only usefully interest himself in problems arising in a well-defined form out of the lives of the species which he has opportunities of observing in a wild state. Put in so many words these considerations may seem laboriously obvious. That they are not understood is apparent to any detached critic from examination of any ornithological journal in progress.

AVOIDING WASTE OF TIME

As to the first limiting factor, the only sure way of avoiding waste of time through duplicating previous work is to make a rule of getting up the literature on any problem which seriously attracts your notice. Many observations remain in manuscript scattered about the world, while others appear in such obscure publications, under such misleading titles, or so entangled with quite different subjects that they are almost as tedious to discover. Getting up literature is accordingly a difficult and unsatisfactory task, and is made possible only by two welcome aids. The first is the printed index and abstract. Every year the Zoological Society of London brings out its *Zoological Record*, in which the section *Aves* catalogues under Region, Species and Author, cross-references all the published papers on birds in recognised scientific periodicals during the preceding year, thus providing a convenient and fairly up-to-date complete key to what has been written about any point both at home and abroad. Another labour-saving device which ought to be far more generally known is the series of abstracts by Charles Elton, of the Department of Zoology, Oxford, which have appeared since 1928 under the title *Notices of Publications on Animal Ecology* in each issue of the *Journal of Ecology*. Here not only the longer current papers but brief notes dealing with bird ecology, behaviour, food habits, numbers, migration and so forth are indexed with a brief description of what they are about which saves much pursuit of useless clues on the one hand, and much overlooking of relevant work on the other. The scope being confined to the British Isles makes for convenience and compactness. The second aid in the tedious business of ascertaining what has already been done is a personal one—the wide and accurate knowledge and generous desire to help of the few men whose special business it is to keep abreast of these matters, and especially of the staff of the Bird Room at the Natural History Museum in South Kensington, where anyone genuinely working on ornithological problems of any sort is welcomed and put on the right track for learning what the nation's reference resources have to offer him. It is, of course, true that any bird-watcher capable of first-rate work may chance repeating what has been done before and get away with it : the penetration of his attack and the originality of his outlook will guarantee that in covering the same ground as others he will find what they have missed and give fresh definition to an apparently exhausted subject. All the same, no one, however good an observer, can neglect previous work without the penalty of wasting much time on useless repetition and, more serious still, of missing repeated opportunities to check statements which have been made which may not stand investigation, but which he may read too late to examine and refute.

CHOOSING RIPE SUBJECTS

This, perhaps, is all that need be said about the necessity for basing each essay in bird-watching on what has been done before. It is, after all, an elementary point compared with the next one—the need for selecting problems advanced enough to be still unsolved, but not so advanced that attempts at their solution are deemed to failure for want of relevant data from other fields. It is easily forgotten that whether the bird-watcher works as an individual out of touch, perhaps, with any other human being who knows one bird from the next, or as a member of an organised team, he is in any case, whether he likes it or not, engaged in a co-operative undertaking. Every time he so much as calls a bird by its right name he is drawing on the common stock accumulated by the systematic labours of past generations of ornithologists : every time he writes or communicates a single fact which he has observed he is potentially adding to that common stock himself. There is, in fact, no such thing as an independent bird-watcher : there are only organised bird-watchers and disorganised ones. From this standpoint it becomes apparent that the danger of going too slow, and merely repeating what has been done before, is balanced by a danger of going too fast and trying to ascertain things the basis for ascertaining which remains to be built. To take a simple case, it would be quite futile for a bird-watcher on a desert island to undertake an elaborate study of territorial habits before he had cleared up the distinctions between the species he was dealing with, so that he could be sure of their identifications. Migration, probably, makes the most spectacular case of the dangers of trying to go too fast. For generations attempts have been made to work out elaborate theories of migration, what causes it, how it is performed, how the route is followed and so forth. Yet the simple concrete data indispensable for any such theory—the actual speed and height at which birds fly, actual movements traced by marking, actual behaviour of birds experimentally released in country unknown to them, or detained until after the season of their normal migration—all these and more are only just beginning to be investigated. It is evident that quite nine-tenths of the speculation and controversy on migration which has occupied the last two centuries has been discreditable nonsense which those responsible could have avoided if they had not preferred airy generalisations to the more searching job of finding out their facts. It has then to be recognised that for each generation bird-watching has its growing points, and that to wander too far from these growing points, either into the past or into the future, brings the penalty of futility. The question immediately arises : what are the growing points of bird-watching at the present time ?

They are, fortunately, varied and interesting. Enough has been done by now to give a basis for effective work in a large number of amusing fields : enough has not been done to bring the cramped feeling which must follow when the age of discovery in bird-watching comes to an end, and is succeeded by an enforced concentration on detail. On several of the living questions of bird-watching this discussion has already touched ; they have formed the background for indicating how bird-watching is done. Some of the rest can be indicated here, but to deal with them at length is clearly impossible : most of them in themselves give material for volumes.

LIFE AND MIND OF THE INDIVIDUAL

The most fundamental of all is the problem of the life and mind of the individual, which may now profitably be tackled with the new resources of psychology, as Eliot Howard has begun tackling it in his *Introduction to the Study of Bird Behaviour*.

THE ART OF BIRD-WATCHING

Whatever other subject may attract the bird-watcher it is important that he should take the trouble to gain something like a true idea of bird-mind, since the only alternative is to use a false one. Repeatedly assumptions and interpretations will have to be based on what the bird-watcher imagines to be at the bottom of the bird's behaviour. If he has not consciously mastered the subject he can only draw on his preconceptions, which will probably be anthropomorphic and almost certainly be wrong. The first necessity in interpreting what birds do is strictly to observe the law of economy of hypothesis. Do not jump to conclusions of purpose, memory, or intelligence which are not absolutely demanded by the facts. Do not, above all, mix up the account of what you have observed with the general deductions you choose to draw from it. Keep fact and theory distinct, so that your material can be re-interpreted if necessary in the light of later or fuller research without error or uncertainty. Without pretending to give even a tentative account of bird-mind it may be useful at this point to give a hint of the view of it which appears to emerge from recent work. We are ignorant in a positive sense of what bird-mind is like, but we know what it is not like, and that is the pale imitation of a human mind which many naturalists have up to very lately assumed. While birds are probably by no means automata they are at the mercy of stimuli, internal and external, to an extent not easily overrated. This conclusion comes inevitably from experimental interference. A Black-headed gull whose clutch has been removed will contentedly brood a tobacco-tin ; almost any small bird will bring food in response to the clamour of a young Cuckoo ; a Sparrow, Martin, or Titmouse will repeatedly build nests on a house or in a box where they are repeatedly destroyed by human beings ; a migrant, detained beyond the proper migration season, will show himself completely at a loss, to mention only a few of the best-known instances. In any bird-watching work full allowance must be made for the power of the stimulus and the power of the rhythm.

An illuminating example of that power was observed by the present writer while watching, during the Oxford University British Guiana Expedition of 1929, a nest of the Guiana King Humming-bird (*Topaza p. pella*) which contained two young almost ready to fledge. To quote a description published elsewhere :

The smaller of the two would suddenly grow excited and restless, beginning to heave himself up and down in the nest rhythmically, finishing with the stern higher each time. After anything up to 12 or more pulsations he would finish with the anus well over the edge of the nest and defecate briskly, shooting the excrement well clear. Then he would immediately subside to the bottom of the nest, sometimes working the tongue up and down. Thus the act of defecation made a clear cycle, like the ejectment of other nestlings by a young Cuckoo (*Cuculus canorus*). The larger nestling, on the other hand, defecated in the normal way, apparently as an act of volition without any rhythm, simply protruding the anus over the edge of the nest.

The significance of this observation lies in showing with exceptional sharpness how an act apparently quite purposive and isolated may at a more primitive stage have occurred not merely as an involuntary response to stimulus, but as a single step in an elaborate rhythm the remainder of which served simply to lead up to it and was discarded as it ceased to be necessary.

CONCEPTION OF THE PATTERN

It may be found useful to try to look at various other actions of birds in this light, seeing them rather as patterns, or vestiges of patterns, than as deliberate solutions of a comprehended problem. Consider, for example, various courtship ceremonies. Pairing Mallard follow a regular and clear pattern, beginning with the rhythmic bobbing of heads in unison, which is accelerated until the duck assumes a prostrate position with her neck extended on the surface of the water, when the drake mounts and treads her, both afterwards raising themselves and flapping water over their backs. The elaborate nuptial ceremonies of Great Crested Grebes and Divers, curious in such apparently backward birds, become explicable if they are interpreted as not yet having found emancipation from a tedious concatenation of formal poses necessary for raising the emotional tone where mind is at its most passive. To take instances from different fields, the song and song-flight of the Tree-pipit, properly regarded, are parts of a single pattern finding dual expression in synchronised sight and sound. The building of a nest, regarded as a rational enterprise, is inexplicable in its conformity to type, and in the senseless aberrations resulting from abnormal conditions, like the filling of a belfry with sticks by Jackdaws or the ninefold duplication of a nest by a Blackbird between successive rungs of a ladder. But regarded as a pattern, which begins at the

183

appropriate stage of sexual activity, nest-building becomes easier to follow if not to understand. Then the spontaneous formation of a flock must be regarded as a pattern, and one in which little variation is commonly shown. Carry the argument a stage further and the loud ringing song of the Chiffchaff or Lesser Whitethroat is a selected fragment of the more diffuse and less effective pattern formed by the sub-song. The characteristic hunting tactics of the hovering Kestrel, the quartering Harrier or the dashing Sparrowhawk may be regarded as stereotyped patterns selected as best fitted to their respective foraging conditions. In artificial conditions, and notably in London, the process of forming these patterns may actually be seen at work. Black-headed Gulls, having realised the possibilities of depending on food from human sources, cease to pick it up in a normal way from the water or the ground, and begin to take it in flocks on the wing, circling in a continuous figure-of-eight past the person who brings something for them to eat. Starlings, discovering the advantages of roosting on large central buildings, develop spectacular flock-patterns with their regular halts, fly-lines and dormitories.

It would be a delusion to suggest that this conception of the pattern solves any mysteries : you do not dispose of a problem by calling it by a new name. What it does is to cut clean across the anthropomorphic tendencies ineradicable from descriptions of bird behaviour in terms of human. If you look at the actions of birds as patterns, and not as history, you will avoid either much error or at any rate much anxious guarding against error. It is, moreover, possible to discern without extravagance in this conception of rhythmic pattern a basis for interpreting bird-mind more deeply.

INTERPRETING BIRD BEHAVIOUR

Considering bird behaviour as fundamentally composed of a series of simple or complex patterns which in turn take control of the individual it is evident that there must be natural selection in favour of (*a*) the individual or species capable of choosing the right pattern to follow in abnormal circumstances, where the straightforward sequence fails to carry him through, and (*b*) the individual or species capable of cutting out these parts of the rhythm which serve only to lead up to the essential act or acts in it, and of performing the latter with little or no preliminary. A familiar instance of (*a*) is the clash of stimulus occurring when Swallows or Swifts try to rear exceptionally late broods, and the migration urge becomes so strong that the young are deserted in the nest. Presumably individuals making the biologically mistaken choice of standing by their young run great danger of paying for it with their lives, and accordingly being selected out. For a hypothetical example of (b) most bird-watchers will remember cases where a stalked bird, although suspicious, has not been quite alarmed enough to fly, but has shown its uneasiness by a constant jerking of the head, and so forth. It is easily understandable that on the assumption that if such a rhythm were in any species a regular preliminary to flight in case of danger those individuals which made the fewest movements prior to the essential springing into the air would oftenest survive, while those which could only take flight after a rhythmic impulse would tend to be selected out.

There is, then, a clear advantage in superseding the elaborate pattern by the simple one, or more ambitiously by a mind capable of acting to some extent independently. It is, like education, a question of readjusting the innate balance. With a rhythmic pattern governing the course of action mind undoubtedly exists, but only as the fettered accompaniment of the various motor discharges occurring. It is a condition humanly reproduced in sudden emergencies—say when a man just stops short of treading on a snake. He stops by an instant reaction of the nerves : mind in a developed sense only perceives what has been done afterwards. Given this pale reflection of a mind in the primitive bird, the way of progress evidently lies in driving a wedge between it and the settled rhythms so that it becomes eventually conscious, capable of memories and simple pictures of other places, or of acts done at other times, and, as Eliot Howard has shown reason to believe, of some vague generalisation capable of giving it unity of response towards a set of otherwise unrelated stimuli.

It is important for bird-watchers to give frequent consideration to this fundamental problem. We may not know precisely what the mind of a bird is like, but we do know with reasonable precision within which psychological strata it is to be found, and any work touching on bird-mind which is done from now on without adequate appreciation of these limits must prove, like too much in bird-watching, to be obsolete before it is undertaken. It is true that the timelag in ornithology is so excessive that probably until well after 1950 the facts which are being tested by current experiment will not have sunk in among the general resources of accepted opinion. Nevertheless it is discreditable, and in the long run fatal, to neglect mastering the background which recent research has put at our disposal, and against which our work must sooner or later be judged.

It is not, of course, to be expected that any ordinary bird-watcher will be able to devote himself usefully to study of the life and mind of the individual, which involves psychological and biological training. All that he can attempt is to keep up with the major discoveries in this field and apply them himself in less formidable provinces.

COURTSHIP PROBLEMS

For example, what is generally described as courtship makes a promising field for further study, in spite of the amount of attention which has lately been given it. Here it is necessary to observe strict concentration on individuals. The Grebes on a single sheet of water, the Swallows about a farm, the Blackbirds or Robins in a large garden, even the House-sparrows about an urban building make the appropriate unit for such observation. What is simplest, and accordingly least likely to be original, is recording the actual ceremonies in use, the pattern they follow, hours, dates and frequency of occurrence, reactions of the participants and so

LITTLE TERN: EARLY DAYS OF INCUBATION. THE MALE IS SITTING ON THE NEST; THE FEMALE HAS PICKED UP A LARGE PEBBLE WHICH SHE WILL SOON CAST ON ONE SIDE.

(By Courtesy of Sir Thos. Lewis, F.R.S.)

forth. It will be profitable to do these things but also to go deeper. How, for instance, does the courtship situation arise? In gregarious species does it precede or follow disintegration of the flock, where that occurs? In territorial species, is the cock settled on his territory before he attempts to mate, and if so does he attempt to court any passing hen, or only some of them, or does he await the arrival of the mate of last season? Is courtship and display an individual affair, or is it communal and restricted, perhaps, to definite *leks* comparable to those of Blackcock, or of some species of Hermit Humming-birds (*Phaethornis*). At what stage in the reproductive cycle do activities of this type begin, reach their peak, and end? Where post-nuptial display occurs, what differences can be detected between it and the earlier demonstrations? What specific notes, gestures, or flight-forms are wholly or mainly associated with courtship?

It would be wearisome and interminable to continue such lists. Enough has been said to indicate the type of questions which the bird-watcher must constantly be asking himself. In framing such questions care must be taken to see that they are relevant to present research. As has already been argued, it is futile to set oneself the problem, for example, of the different types of display and courtship behaviour associated with mating for life as compared with ephemeral matings, because in no case are data yet available on anything like an adequate scale as to which species do regularly or occasionally mate for life and which do not. That is a problem for perhaps 1952 or 1962, and it is only with those problems which can profitably be tackled in 1932 that this tentative and elementary survey is concerned.

If it is conceded that the bird-watcher in advance of his time is liable to be as obstinate a nuisance as the bird-watcher who lags persistently behind it, the lines which ought to be followed at any given moment become remarkably clear. Abandoning records of first appearances, and albino Rooks and erythristic clutches of Tree-pipits' eggs to the antiquarian-minded, and large sweeping theories of the origin of migration and the utility or otherwise of birds from an agricultural standpoint to the imaginative, we find in front of us a number of obvious tasks which need doing without delay, because ornithology will be held up at that point until someone undertakes them. Several of these tasks have already been mentioned : the investigation of bird population, of bird ecology, of the organisation of communities, of territory, of the outline of bird-mind, of breeding-habits, of song,

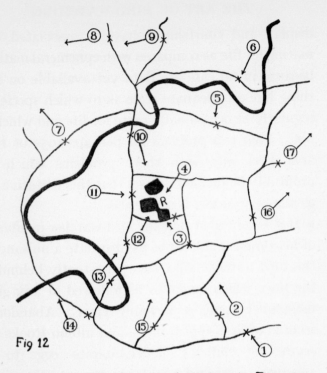

Fig 12

Sketch-map to illustrate method of locating and mapping roosts. The numbers attached to each arrow show how the position is gradually ascertained. No.1 flock is met by chance flying to roost in the direction shown, the observer's standpoint being indicated by an X on the road. With this clue he posts himself farther up the line of flight till No.2 confirms the direction. He then goes much farther on and actually locates the roost R. through the arrival of flock No.3. Flock No.4 appearing from a new direction gives a new line of flight to be followed, this time outwards from the centre. Having traced this line back to 6 search is made along other routes, where flocks 7,8, and 9 are found to be heading for a different roost off the map. The division or "watershed" between the roost R and the next one is therefore approximately traced. Returning, 10,11,12, and 13, fill in the foraging grounds of roost R in the remaining direction, while 14 evidently belongs to the roost still undiscovered off the map. Finally 16 and 17 prove to be heading for a third roost. Thus the foraging area of roost R. is ascertained and the mapping of neighbouring roosts can proceed by the same system, casting about for flocks travelling on likely lines and following them up in a series of stages till the actual roost is located. With a car or even a bicycle, quite large areas of country can be surveyed by these methods, which are applicable to all birds resorting to common roosts from a distance. Roads are shown by thin black lines, a river by a broad winding streak, woodland by a black patch.

of fertility, mortality and disease, of diet, of homing ability, of height and speed of flight, of distribution and so forth are among them. The field is colossal, and the difficulty is to select in advance the part of it which one can most usefully work.

THE LOCALITY DECIDES THE WORK

This selection should be guided by the locality and circumstances in which observation has mostly to be carried out. No one, naturally, would be so misguided as to devote himself to the investigation of communities unless he had opportunities of observing in some place where at least one well-marked communal species was present in reasonable force. Yet errors hardly less crude are committed on an appalling scale. There is, in particular favoured areas such as Blakeney or Fair Isle, a certain amount to be said for intensive observation of rare species on passage. But every year, for one bird-watcher who gives his time usefully to this pursuit at least ten waste their leisure on scouring provincial reservoirs, marshes and sewage farms on the off-chance that some quite ordinary bird, which happens to be rarely recorded in that district, may happen to be met with. The bird-watcher must accordingly ask himself from time to time not

N   193

merely, *Has this all been done already ?*—and *Is this likely to lead anywhere at the present time ?*—but also, *Is this the most sensible line for me to follow in this place and in these circumstances ?*

If all bird-watchers could be brought to face this last question without prejudice or prevarication most of them would have to give up what they are now doing to-morrow, and to take on something quite different. It is of paramount importance to understand that each locality has its own appropriate subjects for investigation, which are further limited by the conditions under which the bird-watcher must work. For example, a business or professional man living in a town, with very restricted opportunities for getting away, and perhaps only an occasional spare hour available, ought evidently to devote himself to the urban bird population around him, recording the fluctuations and density of numbers, the gradual eviction to the outer suburbs of such forms as the Rook, Swallow, House-martin and Jay, the gradual consolidation of a new urban avifauna, including probably such forms as Starling, Moorhen, and Wood-pigeon. He might also profitably inquire into the changes in diet, roosting-habits, competition, parasitism, enemies, and so forth incidental to the artificial existence led by the town birds, and especially into

194

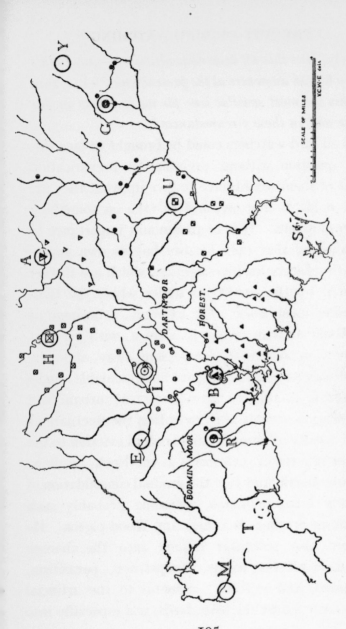

Fig 13. Map of area investigated by V.C. Wynne-Edwards in Devon and Cornwall. Starling roosts are marked by circles, each with index mark in centre. The distribution of the smaller index marks indicates extent of the feeding areas.

SCALE OF MILES

V.C.W-E 6611

195

fresh local adaptations such as the pecking-off of milk-bottle lids by Titmice, parasitism of Black-headed Gulls, on Tufted Duck, destruction of flowers of particular colours, perching on buildings or using strange nesting material. If, however, this same hypothetical town bird-watcher has a car and is able and prepared to work a good deal in the early mornings in spring, investigation of territory on some suitable common or copse or other site a few miles out is open as an alternative. If he is free for long enough at week-ends he may choose between a wide range of subjects without finding himself at a serious disadvantage compared with many observers living in the country.

The art of bird-watching includes ability to make the most of different environments, whether they are Good or Bad places for birds in the accepted sense. It demands that bird-watchers with special advantages shall show the vision and energy to take advantage of them. Such special advantages are of many kinds, and are habitually overlooked. The ship's officer has special advantages for studying oceanic birds at all seasons and detecting their migrations, which are largely unknown, the air pilot has special advantages for observing height and speed of flight, the man who is free to take a holiday in May or June for observing territory or breeding habits, even the man who regularly has a spare hour in the same place daily has an opportunity of getting comparable data not shared by the man whose movements are spasmodic.

CHAPTER VI

THE YIELD OF BIRD-WATCHING

What is the use of Bird-watching ?—Relation to Bird protection—
Co-operative work—Recording results.

WHAT IS THE USE OF BIRD-WATCHING ?

In all this discussion we have steadily maintained
one evident assumption—that bird-watching is
worth doing. No doubt only those who are prepared to accept that assumption will have read so
far. All the same it is undoubtedly necessary to
analyse in conclusion, however sketchily, why
bird-watching is worth doing and where it leads.

It is customary now to be impatient with pur-
suits which are taken up for their own sake, and to
demand that whatever is done shall be able to show
some use for itself. One must even play games, not
for enjoyment's sake, but in order to improve the
physique or to keep fit or to make sure that the
nation shall be ready for whatever demands
another war may make on it. From this narrowly
material point of view bird-watching can if necessary be fully justified. It is an occupation particu-

larly valuable in an urban nation, because the qualities it develops are those which the hunter and the pioneer normally have and which the towns-man is normally without. From a purely athletic standpoint many sports impose a stricter training, but team games and athletics accentuate rather than correct the deficiencies of urban civilisation, especially on the psychological side, and bird-watching has most to offer where other sports, with such notable exceptions as angling and wild-fowling, have least.

If bird-watching justifies itself as a sport, it justifies itself even more clearly as a science. With the recent emergence of biology as the spearhead of twentieth-century science all its components assume an added importance, and the bird-watcher has so many important advantages over students in most related fields that his status is rapidly growing and must for some time continue to grow, perhaps ultimately to the point of partly profes-sionalising the subject. For the study of animal numbers and of animal psychology bird-watching has a contribution to offer which would be hard to overrate. As a compensation for the increasing subdivision of ornithology this intimate part which it begins to play in biological progress needs a firmer emphasis. Bird-watchers must make more

frequent efforts to work in collaboration with ecologists, botanists, entomologists and others who can throw light from various angles on their work.

RELATION TO BIRD PROTECTION

Apart from such a general bearing, bird-watching has others more particular. It is, for example, through bird-watching that the trend of bird protection policy is principally determined. The relation at present between the theory, the law, and the practice of bird protection in Great Britain is in fact remarkably remote, and it is not improbable that the impact of organised observation may soon shatter the shallow and well-meaning assumptions on which the present attitude is based. The nineteenth-century mentality of the Royal Society for the Protection of Birds still leans on the belief that almost all birds deserve protection because they are useful to man, while the tendency of census and diet investigations is all towards showing that the effects of bird life either for good or ill are much more complex and probably much less important than it has been fashionable to imagine. Bird-watching points so far to the solution of protecting birds generally at all seasons, with specific exemptions of game-birds, wild-fowl

and local pests, in place of the archaic and long-winded lists of species enjoying a nominal legal status of several different grades which has survived since 1880 as the British law.

It is likely that eventually bird-watchers will be compelled to arrive at a coherent and united attitude towards this subject of bird protection. Already the breach between legal restrictions and scientific demands is such that a deadlock must have arisen if the law had not become a dated farce. The law in British Guiana takes account of the necessity of exempting to a strictly limited extent from protective ordinances scientists who require a certain number of specimens for legitimate reasons, but the law in Great Britain does not. It is possible, but certainly discreditable, for bird-watchers to adopt in such cases the lazy live-and-let-live attitude, ignoring the ludicrous protectionists and the equally ludicrous laws. Nothing, in any case, looks like preventing the occurrence sooner or later of a direct clash by which the shabbiness of the tacit compromise must be exposed, and when such a clash takes place bird-watchers will be forced to fight or to accept restrictions which they know to be irrational, and which must severely hamper their work. At which point such a clash will happen is still impossible to

foresee. To suppose that bird-watchers, unlike any comparable set of people, can indefinitely preserve their freedom of action without possessing any sort of charter to guarantee it is an ostrich gesture which may lead to serious results. It must be a lively concern of all observers to bring nearer a common understanding on these matters which will secure energetic and decisive action whenever it may be needed.

CO-OPERATIVE WORK

Discussion of protection, as of so many interests of bird-watching, converges once more on the problem of co-operation. From all sides the old-fashioned splendid isolation of the bird-watcher is becoming untenable. Without necessarily surrendering his freedom he is forced to look for the formation of some sort of organisation which can co-ordinate his efforts, enable him to pull his weight and safeguard his position. In the United States, Hungary, Holland and elsewhere a clearing-house for research is provided by the State : in this country such a solution would be uncongenial, and we must look for some alternative centre of national scope not imposed from above but built up from below. An experiment on these lines has been undertaken at Oxford since the founding of the

Oxford Bird Census in January 1927. Beginning as a co-operative venture of the Oxford Ornithological Society, consisting largely of undergraduate members engaging in systematic ringing through a trapping station in Christ Church Meadow and systematic research on local bird population, the scheme now has a full-time Director, Mr. W. B. Alexander, and is carrying out a survey of rookeries and their economic status on behalf of the Ministry of Agriculture. It is intended to put this undertaking on a permanent footing and to build it up as a clearing-house for bird-watching results in this country, filling, in fact, much the same function for bird-watchers that is supplied by the Natural History Museum for systematists. If the attempt succeeds, a large part of the gap which we are always encountering in bird-watching will be permanently remedied.

RECORDING RESULTS

It is simple and obvious to remark that an essential object of bird-watching must be to find the answers to the questions which most urgently await an answer, and to make them available in the best possible form with the least possible delay. For the individual bird-watcher this problem of

making conveniently accessible the results of his investigations is often one of the most difficult to solve. The results of bird-watching may be preserved only in the memory, or in field notes taken on the spot, or in a fair-copy loose-leaf book, or card-index or journal, or in spoken lectures or papers read before an audience, or in articles, films, pamphlets, books or sections of books, and contributions to scientific periodicals. The drawbacks of relying on memory need no stress. Within two or three days observations of this sort become scientifically useless if they have not been committed to paper. Field notes are often more or less illegible : they should be copied carefully at the first opportunity, if possible into a well-kept loose-leaf book or card-index arranged under species headings, but with subject headings also for special points under investigation. By this stage the observations have been put in a potentially permanent form, but they have not been placed in currency, and so far as other observers are concerned they might never have been made. The next task, then, is to set them in circulation. For this purpose, the spoken word, whether in popular lectures or broadcasting, or in addresses to specialist bodies, is too ephemeral to suffice. Where, however, papers read are eventually published in some recognised series of *Transactions* publication is more likely to be effective, although only the most important examples of this class, such as the *British Ornithologists' Club Bulletin* or the *Proceedings of the Zoological Society* can be relied on to be consulted, or even to be adequately indexed. Elton's *Journal of Ecology* abstracts already referred to are helping to overcome this difficulty, but the weakness of the present machinery is well indicated by the fact that the *Journal of Ecology* is itself a periodical which few ornithologists use. The project for establishing a *Journal of Animal Numbers*, or of animal ecology, promises to make good the maladjustment existing at this point.

Films are in some ways the best of all records of observation, for although it is a delusion to imagine that the camera cannot lie, particularly in the hands of the average bird-photographer, the negative is at least fairly free from the blurring effects of subjective distortion. It is regrettable that there is no sort of national collection of bird photographs comparable to the national collection of skins at South Kensington. Such a collection would be cheap to form and to house, especially since many bird-photographers would no doubt be willing to present sets of prints of their more valuable pictures. If the opportunity is not taken soon,

while many of the pioneer nature photographers are still alive and their sets of negatives available, the difficulty of securing a complete library of this sort will be greatly enhanced by the time it comes to be done. The success of any effort in this direction would depend, of course, on full data accompanying the pictures and on an efficient system of indexing and storage.

There remain as outlets for discussion articles, books and sections of books, and contributions to scientific periodicals. The main advantage of writing articles is that one often gets paid for them, but as a method of recording results there is little to be said for them. With the exception of such borderline cases as *Nature*, the *Field* and *Discovery*, bird material appearing in them stands almost no chance of being referred to by subsequent workers in the same field. Moreover, the form of an article is practically irreconcilable with the form of a scientific paper, and in any attempt to combine the two both must suffer. Since publication in a purely scientific periodical in no way clashes with journalism results of any importance may well be published, if it is desired, in both forms more or less simultaneously. Where the same data are used both in an article and a scientific paper it is, however, important that the scientific paper should

appear first, or at any rate not long afterwards. Failure to follow this rule causes an awkward hiatus when ornithologists must be unofficially aware of results which cannot be officially quoted. To mention a conspicuous instance of this trouble, an author's summary of what appeared to be one of the most valuable investigations of bird population lately carried out in Great Britain was inserted anonymously in *The Times* during September 1928. Those interested were still awaiting confirmation and amplification of the data summarised up to the time of writing these words in 1931. Unlike articles, books combine, at any rate nominally, the advantage of bringing some financial return and of being available for reference. Actually the amount of money to be made out of any serious bird book is negligible, while for reference this method of publication is often cumbersome and expensive. Probably at least half of the bird books at present issued annually ought never to be published : scientifically, they are grossly padded and often contain barely enough material for one or two short papers decently compressed : from the general reader's standpoint they are of no permanent value and often of little interest even at the time : financially, they are uneconomic both for the author and the publisher. Book form should only

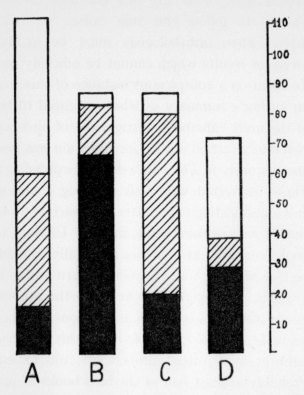

Fig 14. MORTALITY IN THE NEST. Statistics of mortality in the nest which are of the greatest value lend themselves particularly to diagrammatic exposition. The figure shows result for four species A.B.C. and D. The height of the columns represents the total number of eggs and young examined in each case equated against a scale in the margin. The upper section, left white, shows the number of eggs destroyed before hatching, the central section (shaded) the number of young destroyed before fledging and the lower (black) the number fledged "Destroyed" must be taken to cover loss from all causes. It will be observed that while more eggs and young are examined for species A than for species C, species C loses a far smaller percentage before hatching, and in spite of a greater relative loss of unfledged young has a higher effective reproduction rate. By putting figures in this form over several years the results of good and bad seasons emerge in very sharp contrast.

be considered where there is a clear function to be served—an identification handbook, a comprehensive study of some well-defined subject, a discussion of ideas or a contribution to controversy, a regional survey and so forth. Sections of books dealing with birds are often of some value : the *Victoria County Histories* contain instances. Pamphlets show few theoretical advantages, except that they ought to be cheap, and hitherto they have almost without exception failed to exert any appreciable influence on ornithology.

Coming finally to contributions in scientific periodicals ; these have the merit of constituting permanent files which are more or less adequately indexed, and stand probably the best chance of being referred to by others. Such contributions are not as a rule unnecessarily hampered over length and form by the circumstances of publication, and funds sometimes run to providing them with a reasonable amount of illustration by photographs, sketches, diagrams or maps without involving outlay for their writers. In the past such periodicals have not exercised the influence which they undoubtedly could exercise because their contents have frequently been heavy, badly written and pedantic. It is essential that an effort should be made to raise the standard not only of observations recorded but of the style used in recording them. This is a matter largely, of course, for their editors, but also largely for the general body of bird-watchers who have too frequently been content either to leave them to the skin-sorters for catalogue purposes, or to use them as a sort of rubbish-dump for stuff that hardly seemed suitable for publication elsewhere. The *Ibis, British Birds,* and the *Scottish Naturalist* particularly deserve the support of bird-watchers both in consulting what has appeared in them and in supplying them with papers on the best work done in this country as it becomes available.

We must look forward eventually to a clearer division of function to secure the appearance of results of bird-watching in their appropriate regional journals where their significance mainly touches distribution or local factors, or more generalised periodicals where they deal with problems of wider application. There ought also to be a library housing not only all the published material obtainable, but also a mass of indexed manuscripts and typescripts which for one reason or another have not been printed, and are in present circumstances hopelessly lost, since even those who are aware of their existence cannot legitimately refer to them.

THE YIELD OF BIRD-WATCHING

It is important that the results of bird-watching should thus be made available, but these, of course, represent simply the dried husks with which the bird-watcher has no more to do. For those who practise it bird-watching is not only a sport and a science, but also something near a religion, and after all its externals have been inventoried the essence stays incommunicable.

INDEX

INDEX

INDEX

INDEX